EVERY STORY COMES

TO AN END

Snake Bloomstrand

Forward

I became curious about endings after being ambushed by a life-threatening illness. Unexpectedly facing my end, and loitering at the threshold of life, left an enduring mark.

"How close was I to death?" I asked my doctor.

"Less than twenty-four hours," she replied.

I found it near impossible to describe my experience in a string of words. To say survivors "learn to appreciate life" is a gross understatement. In every case the experience is emotional, unique, and personal.

Those of us fortunate enough to step back into life agree we've been forever changed by the experience. The broadest explanation for this transformation is that brushing the end of life reveals valuable insight for the living.

I began interviewing professionals in an attempt to put my experience into words. I chose men and women who witness the end of life daily—morticians, hospice workers, doctors, nurses, and clergy—assuming frequent observers might provide informed insight. I imagined experienced professionals would be well versed and able to speak of endings with authority, but their awkwardness became apparent immediately. We tend to avoid speaking of endings, and as a result, the wisdom embedded in each ending remains hidden.

Humans value predictability and stability, and we do our best to avoid acknowledging the inevitable end of what we depend on or are attached to. Might our emotional stability rely on a measure of denial and our ability to pretend our homes, jobs, and lives and what we love will never end?

As I examined the end of life, a much larger picture took shape. End of life turned out to be the tip of the iceberg, and my stories take a reader deeper. Endings come in all shapes and sizes and are inextricably woven into the fabric of life. Seasons swell and recede, crops are planted and harvested in a predictable rhythm. Babies grow into adults, then return to the earth, wrinkled and worn.

Everything mankind builds or imagines promises a beginning, middle, and end. Great cities and civilizations adhere to this cycle. We tinker with this concept when it suits us, nurturing a childlike hope we can make permanent what was always fated to be temporary, willing to invest in "forever" and neglect the endings. Deep inside we know better. A recent advertisement for cemetery plots promises "perpetual care." Impossible! Eventually every story comes to an end. This collection reveals the neglected wisdom endings offer.

When we examine endings, a greater appreciation grows for the beginning and middle of all things. We complete the loop of an ancient cycle that will not be denied.

Endings matter.

CONTENTS:

Launch a Canoe

I left my Mother's house at sixteen and wandered the world in search of wise men. Twenty years down the road, I've met a few.

Harper never looked especially wise but looks are often deceiving. When he called, asking me to come north to the lake because "we need to talk," I packed my bag.

A legendary character on the north shore of Lake Superior, Harper was nearing seventy. His log home spanned a wide crack in the cliff face high above the lake. Anchored like a treehouse midway up the canyon, the logs seemed to grow from the stone. Harper designed the house, felled the trees, and lowered logs into the crevice using a crane salvaged from an abandoned copper mine. He often joked that operating the crane was what caused his unruly hair to turn white.

Barrel-chested and bowlegged, he claimed his stocky build was an inheritance from his French voyageur ancestry and well suited to the dangerous work of logging massive trees from the northern woods. The Harper family lived on the bluff over the lake long before statehood was declared and mixed enthusiastically with the native Ojibwa tribe. No telling how many bloodlines combined to build the family. His ancestors were powerful men, able to pack two or more ninety-pound packs of cargo over rocky terrain, yet short and stocky, so they wouldn't take up precious space in the freight canoes that carried furs across the lake.

I was road-hypnotized after four hours on the interstate and grateful to finally pull onto the gravel road leading to Harpers Bluff. I opened the windows to let white pine and cedar perfume the car and followed the narrow road along the edge of the bluff. I drove slowly, the lake on my left stretching to the horizon and a dense wall of birch and pine on my right. I parked my Jeep next to Harper's truck, grabbed my pack, and climbed the moss-covered path to the canyon.

Words failed to describe his cabin. The path ended abruptly at the edge of the bluff, where wide stairs were quarried into the rock face and descended forty feet to the log platform supporting the cabin. From above it appeared as if the whole construct had slipped off the edge and wedged tight halfway down.

Harper was sitting on the deck, peeling apples with a paring knife. He didn't look up when I walked across the deck to greet him. "Go to the kitchen and get a knife. We're peeling apples. I'm making applesauce." He instructed abruptly.

I dropped my pack in the front room and, as always, experienced a sense of awe as I entered the cabin. An enormous dark blue and crimson Persian rug covered the pine floor stretching from a wall of lakefront windows to a thick stone counter, which separated the kitchen from the main room. Log walls made up the remaining three sides of the structure, supporting an iron staircase and balcony leading to three small sleeping rooms in the loft.

Wood timbers shaved smooth with a drawknife, granite, and iron display the raw colors of nature, creating a Spartan atmosphere. The glass allows the sun to sweep across the thick carpet, adding majestic warmth to the main room. I grabbed a knife from the kitchen and joined Harper on the deck. He greeted me. "Good to see you, Craig. Glad you drove up."

"Glad to be back," I replied. "It's been awhile."

He stood, stretched his back, and looked out over the lake. "You've been in my dreams," he said accusingly. "Do you remember what we talked about when you were here last?"

A lump formed in my throat. I knew what he was talking about. I'd re-played our previous conversation in my mind driving north today. "I remember." A woven cattail basket full of apples sat on the deck. I selected one and began peeling in an effort to avoid

3

his eyes.

It was spring when I'd last been here, and a wild storm was breaking up the lake ice. We'd sat on the deck late into the night, wrapped in heavy wool blankets, sipping scotch from old herring jars and watching the waves lift four-foot thick slabs of ice high in the air and smash them to splinters on the rocky beach.

He'd questioned me about my life that evening in his characteristically blunt manner. "Are you doing what you're meant to do?"

I was a husband and father. My work was satisfying, and I'd achieved a measure of success. My home life allowed me the sense of belonging a family provided. I listed my achievements: happy kids, money in the bank, all the outside measures we normally apply to success, but he kept asking, "Yes, but are you doing what you're meant to do?"

His question had roamed about in my brain for the last six months, kicking up dust and causing mischief. I still didn't have an answer, and time spent ruminating did little but make me feel uneasy and anxious. I examined the life I'd built and the responsibilities I'd shouldered with a critical eye, wondering whether I'd made the right choices or just played it safe, adhering to a common script. To be honest, the most disturbing revelation? I became convinced if I spent the next forty years simply maintaining what I'd already achieved, I would go insane. I had little cause to feel unhappy, but a restless agitation kept me awake at night. I felt as ripe as the apples we were peeling.

"Last spring, I asked you the most important question a man can ever consider." He stood with his back to me, hands resting on the iron railing. "Put down your knife and come over here."

Standing at the edge of the deck always made my stomach lurch. Fifty feet below, the surf beat a slow rhythm on the smooth fist-sized and larger stones.

"See that canoe on the beach?" he asked.

"Yes." A dented old Grumman canoe lay upside down on the sand, nestled between two large boulders. "Look at me." He unexpectedly put his hands on my shoulders and gazed deep into my eyes. "I see something valuable in you. Can I help you get at it?"

Uncertain how to respond, I backed away, but his hands held me in place. His eyes had a quality I'd seen before, electric and riveting.

"Life is as broad and deep as this lake, but a man must launch his canoe and commit to a direction, not simply drift aimlessly. I want you to choose a direction and find your purpose. That's why I asked you to come to the lake. I saw you struggle with my question, and I've been thinking about you since spring. This is important. I'm not screwing around. Answer me. Will you accept my offer? Allow me to help launch your canoe?"

He released his grip and took a step back. The best response

I could muster was, "Thanks. I appreciate the gesture." I felt self-conscious, as if he had peered into a private part of me I didn't fully understand. I felt both affirmed and challenged by his words.

"Yes or no?" he demanded. "I need to know before we proceed."

"Well c-certainly," I stammered. "I trust you and believe you see something I may benefit from, but how?"

"Not your worry. Follow my instructions and be ruthlessly honest with yourself." He added, "Let me be clear. Do you agree to follow my instructions without question?"

"Yes." Irritated, I said, "You're serious. I get it. I'll do as you say."

"Great. Now go take a nap." He smiled. "You must be tired from the drive, and it's going to be a long night."

Harper returned to his basket, picked up his knife, and pointed in the direction of the cabin. "Go."

I rolled my sleeping bag out on one of the honeycomb-like bunks in the loft. I was tired from the drive and grateful to stretch out for a nap. Before I fell asleep, I remembered Harper's eyes.

I'd seen them spark like that before. Once, while bow hunting, he'd downed a huge buck. Before we field-dressed it, he'd chanted a prayer of gratitude for the life of the buck and venison to last the winter. Months later we were tending a sweat-lodge fire. I dug a pitchfork deep into the fire and balanced red-hot stones on the tines while he swept them free of ash with a bundle of fresh cedar. He'd made eye contact after each stone was clean enough to pass into the lodge. His eyes had glowed like embers.

I awoke an hour-and-a-half later to the smell of apples boiling on the woodstove. I lay in my sleeping bag, mesmerized by the beautiful scene outside the window. The canyon walls framed the eastern horizon, and the lake had become a sheet of glass. Small waves rattled the gravel at the water's edge. The sound, much like an inhale and exhale reminded me the lake is alive.

The metallic whisper of steel cables against a flywheel, and the clatter of the lift, caught my attention. Harper was headed down to the beach. Initially used to lower three miners and their gear into the depths of a mine, the re-purposed lift carried Harper or his guests from the deck to the beach below. The four-foot square cage rose through a trapdoor cut in the rear of the deck and mounted on rails anchored in the canyon wall.

I pulled on a heavy sweater, laced my boots, and climbed down to the kitchen. A five-gallon pot of apples simmered next to a large coffee pot on the flat iron surface of the woodstove. I poured a cup of coffee, checked the firebox, and wandered through the cabin to the front windows.

Harper was more mysterious than usual. I'd had an inkling he was up to something when we spoke on the phone, but I trusted him. Over the years I've seen him go to war against developers intent on destroying the beauty of the north shore and shed tears when a bear saw fit to lie down and die of old age on his beach. We'd buried the bear under a stone cairn, and Harper wept like a child. I'd follow him most anywhere. Now it seemed a certainty he would lead me inside myself. On the way out, I filled a thermos with coffee, grabbed an extra cup, and a bag of oatmeal cookies from a breadbox on the counter.

Harper's sense of humor was displayed on the stainless panel backing the brass lever controlling the lift. Two words were painted in gothic script. "Ascend" had been painted in blue at the top with angels and clouds above the text, and "Descend" was painted in red amidst flames and a devil holding a pitchfork. I stepped into the cage, swung the lever to the down position, and with a lurch, the lift lowered me to the floor of the canyon.

Gravel carpeted the narrow space between the vertical walls before opening onto the wide beach. Harper was dragging large pieces of driftwood across the stones and stacking them in a pile next to the fire pit.

"You need any help? I asked.

"No, I think I've gathered enough to get us through the night. I will take some of that coffee though."

I poured a cup and passed it to him.

"Would you start the fire?"

"I'd be glad to." I stacked kindling and sparked a flame

while he settled on a wide flat stone with his cup.

One can rely on Lake Superior to offer up wind. Gale-force winds frequently assemble on the water and blow ocean-sized waves ashore. Tonight, a glass-smooth lake stretched before us, reflecting a spectacular sunset.

The dry wood caught with very little coaxing, and within minutes a crackling fire sent a vertical column of smoke high above the beach. A downslope breeze filtered through the trees and swept the edge of the bluff, pushing the thin line of pink smoke out over the bay.

"Sorry I was so abrupt earlier." Harper apologized. "I appreciate you understanding my solitary lifestyle makes me a poor host. Honestly, the older I get, the harder it is to be polite. I'm a cranky old man. Cousin Thea came by to visit last week and left in tears after I told her I'd heard enough gossip to last a lifetime."

"I appreciate the apology," I answered, "but I know you're a jerk."

He smiled and poked at the fire with a stick. "Four elders will be joining us for the evening. Their fathers had a conversation with me many years ago, and I'm grateful. It seems the least I can do is pay the debt forward. You've met them at ceremonies we've attended, but more importantly, they know you and were eager to speak with you."

"Is this about my purpose?" I asked. "Or choosing a

direction? Frankly, I don't understand why this has become so important to you. I'm willing, but I have to ask. Am I completely blind to some big awareness? If so, just lay it out. You've obviously let this get under your skin but why?"

"Can you look me in the eye and tell me it hasn't been on your mind?"

"It has," I replied, agitated. "I don't have any clear answers, and the more I think about it, the more confused I get."

"Exactly why we're sitting on this beach tonight, waiting for some old men to show up. I don't have an answer for you, and they won't either, but they can help you drag your canoe to the edge of the water." He was amused with his clever metaphor and pleased with himself for orchestrating tonight's ritual.

We sipped our coffee in silence, fed driftwood into the large bed of coals growing beneath the fire, and watched darkness slip across the beach.

"Here they come." He pointed down the shoreline with a stick. I could barely make out four figures trudging slowly across the gravel along the water's edge. As they rounded the bay, I recognized Sam's two wolfhounds, running wide circles around them.

I smiled, realizing Sam and his dogs were among our guests. The wolfhounds were tall, lean, and good-natured, much like Sam. Despite being in his eighties, and slightly bent in the spine, Sam still stood an impressive six feet, five inches tall. He greeted me with a bear hug. "Good to see you, Craig. We brought dinner."

A fisherman named Art flashed a broad smile and opened the oilskin he carried proudly, displaying a bundle of smoked, lake trout fillets. Harper brushed the ash from a flat boulder near the edge of the fire and carefully laid the fish out to warm on the hot stone.

I'd last seen these men when we'd re-roofed a "cousins" house a year ago. Sam, Art, Lloyd, and Harlan had impressed me, shouldering fifty-pound bundles of shingles up ladders and climbing across the roof, surefooted as squirrels.

Harper left us to get re-acquainted and returned from his cabin fifteen minutes later with the coffee pot, extra cups, and several large loaves of rye bread under his arm. He pulled a wide driftwood plank from the jumble of firewood to use as a cutting board and split each loaf lengthwise with a large knife. Using the blade to lift the oily fillets off the hot stone, he placed each one neatly on the bread, reassembled the loaves, and sliced them into sandwich-sized pieces. "Grab some food and sit down. We've got a lot to talk about."

The old men chastised Harper for being "so damn bossy," and teased one another in a good-natured way as they grabbed sandwiches and coffee. Much like hungry children eager to eat, they settled among the boulders with their bread and oily fish. Distracted from the rodent hunt by the smell of warm fish, Sam's wolfhounds lost interest in nosing among the rocks and lay at our feet, hopeful for a handout.

"We are here tonight to hold space for a man who may have fallen asleep," Harper declared.

Art suddenly stood up. "Let's clean up a little before we begin anything." He pulled a thick braid of sweet-grass from under his coat and lit one end in the bonfire. "You all be quiet for a minute, quit stuffing your faces long enough to catch a breath, and look around." Walking slowly around the circle, and fanning the sweet-grass with a battered old fedora, he thoroughly washed each man with smoke.

I felt a welcome shift take place as Art drew attention to our physical surroundings. "Feel the ground beneath your feet," he said, reminding us to get present and be aware. "Feel the heat of the fire on your face and cool air pushing against your back. Breathe in the smell of sweet grass and breathe out gratitude for good food, wise men, and a beautiful evening." Art laid the smoldering braid next to the fire and sat with his back against a boulder.

With few words Art gracefully set the intention for the evening, replacing the initial meet and greet banter with what felt like something close to reverence. Five weather-beaten faces focused their attention on the light of the fire.

"It seems respectful to offer a song and invite the wisdom and guidance of the ancestors." Lloyd sang out in a deep resonant voice, Sam picked up the familiar Ojibwa chant, and the two voices harmonized. Invitation complete, they ended with a loud shout that echoed off the bluff before fading to silence. The only remaining sound was the crackling of the fire and whisper of water in gravel, until the mournful call of a loon reached our ears from up the shoreline, as if to chime in "Hallelujah!"

I wondered what would come next as the six of us finished our meal in silence. I imagined they had a challenge in store for me, and I felt excitement building in my chest.

Harlan spoke up, as if reading my mind. "Harper cares a great deal for you, Craig. He's never been very graceful around people, but you should know we are here because we all want to see you thrive. We understand Harper's question has been troubling you. What's more, we've all wrestled with the same question. 'Are you doing what you're meant to do?'

"As young men, we did what we were supposed to do. School, jobs, responsibilities, yet we often felt adrift and purposeless, simply going through the motions. A man must identify his purpose and use it to fuel his heart. Understand this is the difference between a man who sleepwalks through life and one who claims life with courage and resolve.

"Are you ready?"

Harlan's words rang true. I did feel adrift, anxious, and in the dark as to where they were leading me, but I was also deeply moved these old men I'd come to admire and trust had taken an interest in me.

"Yes," I answered.

Lloyd picked up the thread. "We can't tell you what your purpose is or what you will find significant enough to justify driving a stake in the ground. The answer is tangled between your head, heart, and soul. We intend to re-pay a debt owed to the elders, who asked prickly questions and awakened us from slumber. You may not return home with an answer, but you can end the sleepwalking and begin the crossing tonight. We are here to send you off on your journey, and we will stay here to welcome you back."

"It's time. Enough talking. Let's send him off," Harlan interjected. "Craig, you tend the fire while we prepare."

My guides stood and picked their way slowly across the beach, entering the dark canyon in silence. I heard the clatter of the lift carrying the men up to Harper's deck but could see little except the silhouette of the bluff against the night sky. Lanterns were lit, and the men moved about the cabin. In ten to fifteen minutes, the lift returned to the beach. The scrape of Harper's canoe against rock confirmed what I'd suspected. They were sending me onto the lake.

Harper led the way, carrying a large bundle, and the men followed with the canoe, two on either side, gripping the gunnels and setting it down gently at the water's edge. Harper laid the bundle in the canoe. "Lloyd, explain what we are doing."

Lloyd stepped forward, reached into the canoe, and opened the bundle. "We gathered some supplies for you." I noticed the bundle was actually a large moose hide. "The hide will keep you warm. Two gallons of water and this bag of pemmican and apples will keep you fueled. We've also included a bundle of cedar and sage. Sam thought it wise to include a couple of flares in case you find yourself in the path of an ore ship."

Sam broke in. "The ore boats are making final runs before the lake freezes, so keep an eye out. The ships maneuver slowly, so stay alert it's on you to avoid them. Give them a wide berth, and use the flares in an emergency to let them know you're out on the lake."

"We want you to canoe into the deep water until you can no longer see the lights from shore," Lloyd explained. "Copper Harbor is well over a hundred miles to the northeast, so you have more than enough lake to paddle.

"There comes a time to take stock of the lives we build and question the paths we cut in the earth. Humans are creatures of habit, finding comfort and security in routine, but over time our eyes cloud over, we fall asleep, and fail to see the opportunities or soul tasks laid at our feet.

"When people recognize the glassy eyes of the sleepwalker and make a noise, be grateful. Harper made noise in your world last spring, suspecting you'd fallen asleep. He irritated something deep inside. You are in good company. Each of us have benefitted from awakenings over our long lives. We've all been challenged to step into the unknown with little but a question.

"Tonight, we pay the gift forward.

"Leave with us the responsibilities you shoulder day to day. We will serve as worthy caretakers of what binds you to your life, so unburdened you can better hear the lake speak. Let your soul guide the canoe, and we will welcome you when you return. Seek your purpose free of what you've already built and listen for the voice of the life you're destined to live.

"It's time. Get in. We'd be honored to push you out."

I stepped into the canoe, arranged the moose hide to cushion my knees, and knelt on the bottom. I grabbed the long wooden paddle, looked into Harper's teary eyes, and said, "Thank you."

The keel scraped gravel as they pushed the canoe free from shore. Wading knee deep into the lake, they held me still, suspended in the water, then Art began a voyageur paddling chant. All five men joined in, sliding the canoe back and forth across the surface in time to the rhythm. I recalled hearing the song at a canoe race years ago; French in origin, it set a rhythm in place well suited to the paddling ahead of me.

As the tempo sped up, so did the sawing motion of the canoe. Harper counted, "One, two, three—push!"

Launched free of their grip, I sped silently out into the lake. I looked over my shoulder. Five old men disappeared into the darkness.

"The lake will tell you when to return. Listen to her!" Harper shouted.

I was grateful for the gentle swells, knowing full well the lake could grow hostile without warning. I adjusted my course, aiming the bow slightly north of the rising October moon, and settled into a steady pace, recalling the many times I'd left a familiar shore and paddled a dented old canoe into the unknown.

The Final Touch

I slid behind the wheel of my car at dawn and paused before turning the key. I took a deep breath and steadied myself ahead of the half-hour drive I'd been anticipating for several years.

A phone call had set me in motion that morning. The tone of my sister's voice had said more than her words. "I went in to take Mom her coffee and discovered she'd died in her sleep last night. Would you come out?"

Mom had lived with my sister and her husband the last several years, lingering in the landscape separating life and death. Anticipating her death had hardly prepared us for this moment. The finality that settled in when a life ended still felt like a surprise.

I started my car, backed out of the driveway, and headed for the highway, my mind flooded with memories. Ordinary moments mostly, collected over a lifetime, each significant of the relationship I shared with my mother: ice skating together after school on winter afternoons, reading Grimm's fairy tales before bed, or simply sitting at the kitchen table, listening to the radio as she made spaghetti on Saturday nights.

I sped down the empty highway, and the harsh reality of her death began to seep in. She was gone. I would never speak with her again. Sadness and grief filled the empty space she had occupied in my heart.

My son and I had visited only yesterday. We'd sat for a couple of hours, chatting about all that had been going on in our lives. Her life had grown very small, her passion for mystery novels and needlework had evaporated, and her sole entertainment came from the lives of her children and grandchildren or occasional visits from friends.

A pink sunrise bled across the horizon as I pulled into the drive. All the lights were on in the house, and I could see my sister and her husband in the window, waiting at the kitchen table. They heard my car door slam and met me at the door.

We stood in a small circle in the entryway while my sister explained, "I found her this morning, she looks like she's sleeping."

I was grateful. I've seen lives end in pain or panic. I hadn't wanted her to suffer that fate. She'd earned a peaceful death.

"We called the coroner. They'll be here in an hour or so to

take her body to the funeral home. Do you want to see her?" she asked.

I nodded, hesitating at the top of the stairs leading down to the small basement apartment my mother had made into her home.

"Do you want us to come with you?" they asked.

"No thanks. I'd like to sit with her alone."

We'd often sat for hours, discussing books we had read or speaking about the people that moved through our lives. As I looked around her apartment, I noticed her small collection of familiar objects and furniture that had provided a setting for conversations spanning over fifty years.

Her copper tea set, a wedding gift received when she married my father and favorite easy chairs at one time placed either side of a massive stone fireplace in the large house where I grew up. She'd lived in many houses with these favorite bits and pieces. This morning, surrounded by these familiar furnishings, we would have one last conversation.

Walking into her bedroom without knocking made me feel like I was invading her privacy. She lay on her back, blankets pulled up to her chin as if sleeping. Life had slipped away in the night, leaving behind an empty vessel. When life and breath end, a body takes on a surreal quality, as if life filled it like air fills a balloon, and when it leaves, it appears deflated.

Mom had always been self-conscious about her appearance. I

checked to make sure she looked presentable, knowing she would appreciate the gesture. But as in life, she'd taken care of everything, eyes closed, mouth shut, and one withered hand gracefully resting on top of the blanket. I knelt next to her bed, thinking how odd the silence was and scarcely knew how to be with her without words.

She was raised in a stoic Scandinavian family. I didn't recall ever receiving physical affection from her as a child. I had no doubt I was nurtured and loved, but physical affection was not how she expressed herself. I could count on one hand the number of times we embraced, always during moments of tragedy, and then an uneasy expression of emotion.

Physical intimacy has felt awkward all my life. Uncertain how to satisfy my hunger for the physical affection I'd missed as a child, I vacillated as an adult, resisting and avoiding touch or lavishing physical affection on those I felt close to.

As I knelt beside her bed, I felt compelled to touch her. Smoothing the blanket almost apologetically, I slid a hand under hers and cradled it in mine. Her limp hand, with its paper-thin skin, seemed to dissolve into my rough hand. Tears filled my eyes as I unexpectedly recalled holding hands with her as a child as we crossed a street. Her hand had been young and strong, reaching out to smooth the wild cowlick in my hair or turning the pages of a storybook as I sat in her lap. Common everyday motions made by a mother, caring for a child. The lifeless hand I cradled had once fed, bathed, and nurtured me in countless ways.

Despite the stubborn belief that I had missed out on something, she had indeed touched me. The years I'd spent feeling I had missed out on physical affection appeared to be a tragic misunderstanding on my part. I'd been looking for hugs and kisses and had missed the love and touch this woman offered every day. My long-held story wasn't entirely accurate.

I hung on as memories returned. Her hand pointed to the past, soothing the neglect I'd imagined. This woman, once vital and beautiful, had given birth to me, nurtured and awakened me. My last words to her could only be "thank you" and holding her hand my final act of affection and appreciation.

Years have passed since the morning I said goodbye to her. The momentary uncertainty or unease I experienced sitting with her empty body had transformed into profound gratitude.

The precious moments following death shout loudly of an ending, and if we listen closely, the echo of a life lingers in the room.

Lucy

I bought a dog from a newspaper ad: Airedale, female, pedigreed. One year old. $75.

On impulse I called the number, loaded my wife and kids in the car, and set off to meet the dog. We arrived to find the owner, a young woman, pacing back and forth on her porch. She greeted us nervously and led us into a fenced backyard. Whining and barking came from inside the garage, and the wooden door shook and rattled as the dog leapt against it.

"I'll let her out," the young woman said, looking fearful.

A large Airedale burst out excitedly, jumping in the air and running circles around her. Surprised to find unfamiliar people in the yard, the dog made a beeline straight for my six-year-old son, knocked him to the ground, and grazed his forehead with a tooth in an attempt to taste his face. The dog wasn't aggressive, simply large, awkward, untrained, and capable of generating enough energy to power a small city.

The Airedale ran high-speed laps while the five of us clustered out of harm's way in the center of the yard, listening to the woman's story. She explained the dog had been a gift from a former boyfriend. She'd never owned a dog, but at the time she couldn't resist the cute little brown and black puppy. She suffered serious regrets. The boyfriend had disappeared, and the puppy filled out to sixty pounds and was growing larger every day.

"I'm in school and working. I don't have time to take care of a dog," she said. "I've had to keep her in the garage after she tore up my curtains and chewed the windowsills to splinters." Her elbows were skinned, and large scabs covered both her knees. She saw me staring and explained defensively, "I try to walk her but she's too strong for me. A week ago, she knocked me over and dragged me down the street. I have to find a home for her!" She was desperate and near tears.

The dog circled tirelessly on a two-foot wide path of hard-packed earth, where the grass and flowerbeds had been trampled beyond repair. Her graceful lope demonstrated both strength and endurance. She was magnificent, with a thick curly coat and well-defined black and brown markings. Large for an Airedale, and a bit stir crazy from living in a garage, but otherwise healthy. As the dog slowed, I managed to get her boxed into a corner. She made good eye contact, cautiously stepping forward, curious about the treat I'd pulled from my pocket. I fed it to her slowly and ran my hand over her body. I could feel the tension bottled up in this dog. Her muscles were taunt, refusing to relax in response to my touch.

"Can I take her for a walk?" I asked the owner.

She looked alarmed and reluctantly handed me the leash she'd been clutching. "Please be careful, I wouldn't want you to get hurt."

My wife and children were shocked I was actually considering this wild creature. I grabbed the dog's collar, intending to attach the leash. She yelped loudly and immediately rolled onto her back, legs thrashing the air. I managed to reach between the flailing legs and clip on the leash. The instant I let go of the collar, the dog jumped to her feet and dragged me toward the gate. "I'll be right back," I said, lurching down the driveway to the street.

Walking her was an adventure. I knew enough to take the lead, so I set off at a brisk pace. Still, it was like walking a Tasmanian devil on a rope. She'd pull hard, then reverse, every bird and blowing leaf catching her attention, and she was desperate to chase every car that passed us.

Midway around the block I stumbled upon one of those rare moments of connection possible between man and dog. I stopped just to see what she would do. She pulled against the leash for a minute, realized I wasn't moving, and sat down. She looked me straight in the eye, as if to say, "What's next? I'm waiting!" This was exactly what I'd been hoping to see. She might just be capable of learning to follow my lead someday.

Everyone was sitting on the porch steps when we returned. "What do you think?" I asked my wife.

"She's big," my wife responded cautiously, but her face clearly said, *Are you insane?*

"She could use a little training," I agreed, "but I can work with her. We should give her a chance." I'd already decided on the dog and ignored my wife's reluctance. I suppose her reaction was reasonable. It was an impetuous decision. The dog was large, wild, and going to take a lot of work, and she did bite my son on the forehead, albeit accidentally.

I made a deal with the grateful young woman on the spot, loaded the dog in the back of our station wagon, and slammed the door.

All hell broke loose inside the car. The slam startled the dog. She leapt into the backseat and crashed into my kids, running back and forth across their laps before jumping for the windshield. She hit the dashboard and dropped to the floor between my wife's legs. She made a grab for the dog, missed, and took a hard hit to the jaw from its head. By the time I'd walked around and opened the driver's door, the dog had settled comfortably behind the wheel, wagging her tail and happy to greet me.

My kids were crying, my wife was rubbing her sore jaw, and we hadn't even left the driveway. I grabbed the dog's collar angrily, led her to the back of the car, and tied her this time. No one was happy with my choice except the young woman cautiously peeking through her torn curtains as we drove off. It was a silent ride home, except for the persistent whining coming from the rear of the car.

Our first meeting set a precedent for what would remain a complicated relationship. Lucy grew rapidly with regular exercise and gained twenty additional pounds of muscle. By the time she was two, she weighed well over eighty pounds. I later learned the breeder had developed this special flavor of terrier for bear hunting in Montana. She came from a family of grizzly hunters.

Large doses of exercise and attention calmed Lucy down a bit, but she was a bull in a china shop. Good-natured and loving but penalized constantly for unnecessary roughness. Once she got used to our routine, she fit into our household fairly well. We learned to anticipate her quirky behaviors and peculiar appetites in an attempt to keep her alive.

Her digestive track was remarkable. She developed an appetite for bars of hand soap, forcing us to hide it or she'd eat it right off the drain board and froth at the mouth for days. I'm convinced she was part goat. Nothing upset her stomach, and everything disappeared effortlessly down her throat. Legos, toy soldiers, stones, a large rawhide chew—everything disappeared in an instant.

My kids kept their crayons under lock and key. She had a peculiar habit of chewing on beer cans, empty or full, nibbling the sides of the can into small bits and swallowing them, leaving behind the top and bottom. Cleaning Lucy's dog run each week left me in a state of wonder. The discoveries I made with a rake and shovel left me amazed the dog was still alive.

Humans seldom appreciated Lucy's exuberant approach to life, but dogs strenuously objected. They interpreted her rambunctious behavior as aggressive, forcing me to referee countless fights. Lucy was more than willing to engage. I think she saw each canine snarl-fest as good clean fun and always walked away in high spirits.

Some of her behavior made sense to me, but she often mystified me. Even though I was furious at the time, it made sense when she snatched a fifteen-pound Easter ham cooling on the counter at our lake cabin and ran off into the woods to devour it in private. The smell of ham fresh out of the oven was irresistible.

On the other hand, it made no sense when she refused to run away or even go for a meander on her own. On occasion she would chew a hole in the cedar fence surrounding her dog run and escape. She'd cross the street, sit on the boulevard, and stare patiently back at our house until someone noticed and retrieved her.

I've lived with dogs all my life. Each one helped me mature. Dogs have taught me patience, discipline, tenacity, commitment, and countless other subtle life skills. If I hadn't been so preoccupied with the illusion that I was training her, I might have noticed she had a lesson plan for me.

I enrolled her in an obedience class. I considered myself a competent dog trainer, but the social aspect of a formal class seemed a wise strategy for such an un-socialized dog. Lucy was not a star pupil. Walking from the car to the training arena was an adventure.

Surrounded by twenty other dogs, her excitement reached a level that rendered her incapable of obeying the simplest command. The instructor took pity on us, coaching us after class when things went badly and loading on the praise when we managed to avoid a fight for an entire evening. A small victory but a victory!

When I practiced with Lucy at home, she was brilliant. She performed basic commands that eluded her during class with ease. Of course, by this time we'd attended class for eighteen months instead of the usual ten weeks. Lucy was special.

I arrived at class early one evening, intending to call it quits, and commented to the instructor, "I think Lucy has come as far as I can take her. She's obedient at home, but for some reason class throws her off."

I'd become confident enough to walk her off leash

occasionally, and she performed like a show dog. She'd even learned to be respectful around other dogs, thanks to my neighbor's St. Bernard. The neighbor's dog simply lifted one enormous paw in the air and pinned Lucy to the ground if she got too annoying. I regretted quitting, but the class had become an unpleasant weekly ritual of failure.

The instructor had gone out of her way to help, constantly suggesting creative techniques. She'd grown fond of Lucy and saw real potential, but she was frustrated as well and offered one last idea. "I'd like you to try one more thing. You said at home and off-leash she knows her commands. Tonight, you're going to do the advanced class. Hand me your leash."

I told Lucy to stay, unclipped her leash, and handed it to the instructor, who walked away with it.

"The other dogs will be here any moment," she said over her shoulder with a sly smile. "Good luck."

I went into a panic. People were arriving with their dogs, traditionally a delicate time, and I found myself standing beside a dog whose brain usually emptied the instant class began.

I reached for her collar and commanded, "Lucy, stay!"

The instructor was watching. She raised one finger to admonish me for grabbing the collar and said one word. "Trust."

I let go and gave a firm command. "Lucy, heel." She obeyed, and we marched around the ring, stopping on the far side opposite the entrance. "Lucy, sit."

Her eye contact was excellent, her manners most respectful, and her obedience unshakable the entire evening. She performed like she was competing in the Westminster dog show, all with no leash. I couldn't believe it.

After class I lingered to thank the instructor.

"My hunch paid off," she said with pride. "Lucy resents the leash. She's willing to follow your commands. She's smart and knows what to do and just wants the freedom to choose when to obey. Lucy can do little but follow her instincts and unique nature. Respect her and give her a measure of freedom. My guess is she will reward you with love. Just look at her." Lucy was sitting calmly at my side, looking up at me, waiting to be led to the next adventure.

I drove home from class that evening a happy man. Lucy and I had reached an understanding. Occasionally I would use the leash but found it unnecessary most of the time. Lucy enjoyed pulling, so I traded her collar and leash for a comfortable harness and a long rope. In the winter snow, she pulled me miles through the woods on cross-country skis. I rigged a rope on my canoe, and she swam in front, eagerly pulling me down the river on warm summer days. The dog was inexhaustible, and once I'd learned to respect her instead of trying to control her, our relationship became a pleasure.

I headed for the kitchen early one morning to make my coffee. Normally Lucy was overjoyed to see me and eager to get on with the day, but this morning she was absent. I went into the backroom and found Lucy lying in her bed. Her tail wagged weakly, and she tried to lift her head, but she appeared to be paralyzed.

After some massaging and encouragement, I got her to her feet, and an hour or so later, she seemed to have completely recovered. I made an appointment to see the vet, and after blood tests, he diagnosed her with Lyme disease, a progressive illness that results in nerve damage, bone degeneration, and eventual paralysis. The vet administered a cortisone shot and explained the frequency of her spells would increase over time. Eventually the pain would force me to euthanize her. There was no effective treatment.

Lucy and I enjoyed another year together. She continued to be entertaining and was seldom ill, but as the vet had predicted, her suffering eventually increased. The spells of paralysis came closer together, and I was forced to make the heartbreaking decision every dog owner would rather avoid.

The first few months without Lucy were difficult. I'd grown dependent on her companionship. I walked every evening, but without her company, the exercise failed to satisfy, and I'd often lay awake through the night. It wasn't just that I'd lost my dog. I felt restless and unhappy much of the time.

One pre-dawn morning, I found myself mulling things over and came to the conclusion I'd been playing it safe. I'd accepted a blueprint for life and adhered to it faithfully. I'd gone to school, built a business, and created a family, yet I felt perpetually unsatisfied. Lucy's death forced an upset in my routine, forcing me stop and look inside. One troublesome detail became clear.

The draftsman who had drawn the blueprint I'd been following never had me in mind. Lucy couldn't help but follow her instincts. Unruly and messy at times, but always authentic and willing, she'd made no apologies for her nature.

I'd mistakenly allowed myself to become leashed to a rigid plan. I'd grown into a serious adult so removed from my authentic self that most days I felt like I was on a treadmill, going through the motions.

I had no clue what my true nature might even look like. Worse yet, I couldn't imagine what I might do differently.

Lucy inspired me to slip off my leash. In the same way I came to respect Lucy's nature, I learned to respect my own. The big wild grizzly hunter of a dog led me to liberation, and I'll be forever grateful.

Chew off your leash!

The Irresponsible Heart

I feel a flash of annoyance when my cellphone rings when I'm in the car. "Don't you realize I'm driving?" I want to shout. Of course a caller wouldn't know that. How could they?

Driving cautiously through four inches of slush dropped by the latest winter storm, I was dismayed to see "Hawaii" printed on the screen. Someone is calling from Hawaii? How inconsiderate on such a crappy day.

When I arrived home, I checked my messages. Hubert had left me a voicemail. "Snake, Give me a call. I nearly died last night, I'd like to speak with you."

I've known Hubert for years and the last several we've both endured illnesses and shared many conversations regarding what it's like to live inside a worn or broken body. His message didn't have the shock value it might have once had. Our previous conversations have both hardened and softened us.

Five years ago, Hubert suffered a massive heart attack. Surgeons worked their magic and Hubert's chest became home to an array of sophisticated machinery and electronics meant to assure his wild and irresponsible heart would conform. A reliable rhythm was the goal.

I settled at my desk and returned Hubert's call, assuming this latest adventure had something to do with his heart. He answered after two rings.

"I had the most amazing experience last night. Do you have time for me to tell you about it?" he asked.

"Certainly. First, are you okay?" "I'm fine now, but last night was touch and go," he answered.

I ignored the background sound of wind chimes stirred by a warm Hawaiian breeze and resentfully watched the snow fall outside my window. Jealousy wasn't going to serve either of us. "Tell me your story."

"Late yesterday afternoon my wife and I went to the beach. We'd heard a large pod of whales were calving offshore." He sounded excited. "There were twenty to thirty of them, and the Pacific was as calm as could be. Carole and I spread a blanket on the beach and settled in with our binoculars.

"It was a beautiful evening. You know how quiet it can be, with only the smallest riptide and no waves. I swear I could hear the whales break the water when they surfaced."

"I told you it's snowing here, right?" The scene he described made me long for somewhere warmer than Minnesota.

"Oh, sorry. I forgot," he apologized. "Anyway, we'd been watching the whales for a while when I started having chest pains. They came on fast, and I was frightened at how quickly they spread across my chest and down my arms. I recognized the pain. I knew what was happening. "My first thought was 'Crap, not now.' Not here at the beach, miles from the hospital. I didn't want my wife to go through this alone. Besides, I wasn't ready. I still had so much to do. A long list of unfinished projects scrolled through my brain as I struggled to get a breath under the excruciating pain.

"Carole saw I was struggling, and the panic in her eyes helped me find the strength I needed to stand up. She quickly gathered our stuff and asked if I could make it to the car. I couldn't even respond to her, I was so focused on the vise tightening in my chest. The best I could do was shuffle through the sand to the parking lot. Nearly to the car, I stopped at the edge of the beach next to a cluster of small palm trees. I looked back at the ocean and had the most remarkable vision." He paused.

"Go on," I encouraged.

"It was the most beautiful sunset on the smoothest ocean I've ever seen. The surface was broken by long lazy curves cut by whale backbones, and concentric rings radiated outward when they came up to blow and catch a breath. Each ripple caught the light and stood in contrast, pink curves on a dark blue surface. I pictured the scene from under the water, as if I were swimming among them, and I remember thinking, 'If I die right now, maybe my spirit will reincarnate in a newborn whale.' I could live in the ocean and swim through another lifetime, deep in the sea. A sense of incredible peace washed over me as I imagined myself into the body of a baby whale.

"Snake, I don't believe in reincarnation. All I know is it seemed so real, I just had to tell someone about it. Do you suppose the soul can leap toward a new birth when faced with the death of the body it inhabits?"

"I don't know," I replied, "but I could get behind the notion of being re-born as a baby whale."

"That's not all," he continued. "When I turned away from the ocean and looked at the parking lot, I couldn't believe what I saw. No more than twenty feet away, I watched my wife helping an old man to the car. I was the old man. I'd left my body and was watching from a distance, caught between two worlds and clinging to a palm tree. I laughed, Snake, it was so absurd, I laughed."

"Amazing," I said. "What happened then?"

"I'm sure it was only seconds, but it felt like ten minutes, torn between making the decision to join the whales or return to my wife. I struggled to make a choice, locked in a strange no man's land, weighing my options.

"The pacemaker ruined the moment, suddenly giving my heart a jolt. Felt like a mule kicked me in the chest. I dropped to the ground, suddenly back in my body and lying next to my car, staring at my distorted reflection in the bumper. The electronics in my chest made the choice for me. I still don't know quite what to make of the whole experience."

"And you're okay now?" "Yeah," he answered. "The shock triggered my heart back into a regular rhythm. It was the first time this one fired. My old pacemaker made me feel extremely tired, but this was like a jump-start, sudden and shocking. It took a while for the pain to subside and for me to get my wits about me. I propped myself up against the car and watched the whales circle with a peculiar longing, wondering what choice I would have made if electronics hadn't interfered."

"It's a hell of a story, Hubert," I responded. "Certainly, a different twist on a near-death experience. I've never heard anything like it."

"I knew you'd appreciate it." "Baby whale?" "I don't even know if I believe that type of exchange is possible. It doesn't make any difference though. In that moment, it was perfectly reasonable. If not for the pacemaker, I might be a whale right now, swimming in the pacific with my mother." Hubert laughed. "I was ready to leave this worn old body."

We spent a few more awkward moments on the phone before ringing off. He tried to reassure me he hadn't lost his mind and offered a few comments intended to rationalize his experience. It's impossible to rationalize a near-death experience. The mysteries we stumble across near the end of life are incredible, and Hubert's experience certainly fits in the mysterious category.

I disconnected from Hawaii and watched snow blanket my yard.

Baby whale?

I wondered if the soul could be so fluid or impatient, it might leap instantly to the nearest birth, the nature of spirit so strong, any creature would do.

I hoped not.

In the dead of winter, the only creatures giving birth in my neighborhood are the squirrels and raccoons nesting high in the treetops.

The Pastor

I've driven past this church countless times over the years and learned to avoid the neighborhood on Sundays. Traffic jams caused by the congregation arriving or departing require half a dozen off-duty policemen to work the intersections, safely guiding congregants from their parked cars to the sanctuary and back again. I'm told this is one of the largest Lutheran churches in the United States.

Located in an upper-class residential area, the sheer size of the complex is intimidating. The original chapel is a classic example of limestone and brick architecture popular in the 1920s. Enormous stained-glass windows set in stone stand shoulder to shoulder the length of the building, and a thirty-foot rosette anchors the altar end of the chapel. Each window is a beautiful glass snapshot, capturing a poignant moment in the life of Jesus.

The original chapel is difficult to discern from the larger structure, resting like a jeweled egg in the center of three modern additions. Each addition was built to accommodate extra pews for the thousands of congregants the original architect never anticipated. Like ripples in a pond, the additions have sprouted additions and now house administration buildings, classrooms, community meeting rooms, and a large gymnasium.

A dozen white vans line the parking lot, each one marked with a blue cross and Outreach Ministry printed on the side in large block letters. Apparently, this church has outgrown its hundreds of pews and the pastors have taken to the streets. I'm here to interview one of the many who serve this congregation.

My spiritual education began in a large Lutheran church. I participated in youth groups and camping trips led by young, courageous ministers willing to chaperone pre-teens. As I pass the Events bulletin board in the hallway, I read: **Tubing on Shaddegg Creek, Fri June 27.** The pink, thumbtacked flyer triggers a flood of adolescent memories.

The liturgy is largely focused on the life and teachings of Jesus, and the image of a shepherd became synonymous with Jesus. As a child, I was confused by the stories. I thought I'd heard Jesus was a carpenter, but the pictures more often portray him as a shepherd, guiding humanity to the gates of salvation.

My experience is that Lutheran pastors seem to embody some characteristic of a shepherd. Whether old or young, they lead the congregation, using the moral compass of Jesus's teachings for direction and inspiration.

I found my way to the office and approached the reception desk, anticipating the predictable reaction strangers usually have to my nickname. The receptionist held one finger in the air as she spoke into a headset wired to a large switchboard.

As I waited for her to finish the call, I noticed a custodian washing the windows. Outside in the courtyard was a life-sized bronze sculpture of Jesus seated with children gathered around his feet. The custodian nodded in my direction, expertly wielding a squeegee in one hand and a rag in the other. Colorful tattoos covered his arms, and two-inch discs were embedded in his earlobes.

The receptionist removed her headset. "Can I help you?"

"I have an appointment with Pastor Svendahl," I replied.

"Your name?"

"Snake Bloomstrand." She blinked. "Did you say Nate?"

People often mishear when I introduce myself. "No. Snake, like the reptile."

"Snake," she repeated, saying my name with an exaggerated "ssssss." Avoiding eye contact, she added quickly, "I'll let Pastor Svendahl know you're here."

"Don't worry, my name isn't biblical," I joked.

The receptionist considered whether my joke was at her expense. The custodian erupted in laughter behind me. Silencing him with a sharp glance, she began a flurry of button pushing, connected with the pastor, and announced, 'Mr. Bloomstrand is here.' She looked at me suspiciously, and using a tone just short of a command, instructed me to take a seat. She ran a tight ship; this was clearly her domain.

I roamed the reception area, lingering at a bank of oak bins containing pamphlets on a wide range of topics: Social programs, volunteer services, counseling, and missionary opportunities were displayed for the curious visitor.

Pastor Svendahl entered the room after a few minutes. He shook my hand and invited me to his office. A tall fit man in his late sixties, sporting a thick and expertly trimmed shock of white hair, he wore a striped dress shirt open at the neck and sharply creased khakis.

We walked up a flight of stairs and down a long hallway, making small talk about the beautiful June weather and the thunderstorm that had rumbled through town the night before. I noted how silent the huge building was and remembered it was Monday morning. Sunday is the busy day for a church, and the rest of the week most of the building is empty.

We settled in his office, and I thanked him for taking time to see me, and then explained the nature of my project. "I'm doing interviews with people who work with death and dying on a frequent basis. I'm interested in what emotional pressures and insights professionals discover and how it impacts their personal lives."

He rocked back in his upholstered desk chair, staring at me as if he didn't understand. We had spoken about this on the phone when I made the appointment, so I interpreted his reaction as simply not knowing where to begin. His opening statement confused me.

"Death? It does speak to the great promise of Christianity, doesn't it? The faithful needn't be concerned, Jesus promises everlasting life."

I was taken aback by this declaration and tried to clarify, "Actually, I'm not writing about the afterlife. I'm curious about the last six months or year of life and the emotional impact death has on the living."

"Oh, you wonder how I feel when I make a home visit or do a funeral?"

"Exactly," I encouraged. "Anything you can share is of value."

"Well, let me think. I feel sad at funerals, especially if I know the person or if a child has died. Is that what you mean?"

"Yes, but I'm guessing you experience a wide range of emotions, right?"

"Now that you mention it, the greatest emotional high I experience as a pastor is during a funeral. My job is to create sacred space, whether it's Sunday services or a funeral. The latter is especially moving because I am opening a door for the deceased to be reunited with their loved ones and the Lord. Death is cause for celebration, according to my beliefs." I found the notion of "emotional high" a little disconcerting. I thought I understood what he was saying, but decided to probe deeper. "Can you explain what you experience?"

"It's more a feeling," he said. "Composing a eulogy can be challenging, especially if I don't know the person well. I have to rely on family members or friends to describe the deceased. It's tricky actually, because unless I'm accurate, my eulogy falls flat. I can see it in the reactions of the people gathered.

"It's difficult for a pastor to look at the faces in the congregation and see blank stares meeting his words. If I'm on my game, I feel like I've honored the family of the departed. This makes a funeral different from any other kind of service. Jesus meets death head on. He conquers it. So Christian funerals are not only about celebrating the life of the deceased, they're about the life of Jesus and his promise of everlasting life. Guiding this reunion is a thrilling experience."

It seemed as though Pastor Svendahl was warming up, so I asked my next question. "Several people I've interviewed have mentioned how challenging it is to serve families when a loved one dies. Is this true for you as well?"

"Families do struggle with grief and loss. I do my best to comfort them. Often their pain and suffering cause a crisis of faith. In those moments I remind them of Jesus's words: 'Whosoever lived and believeth in me shall have everlasting life.'"

He kept coming back to everlasting life. I found it difficult to steer him in the direction of death. He seemed reluctant to speak about the end of life, leaping past and returning to the promise of what was to come. I changed my strategy. "What about the conflict survivors experience with one another when a loved one dies? Is that something you see often?"

"It's not uncommon. Families are under a great deal of stress. We have an excellent counseling department available to families. Therapy falls outside my ministry, and I'm grateful for the psychologist and therapists we have on staff. My role is to support the families and strengthen their faith in the teachings of Jesus."

I decided to take a different approach, "What has been your most challenging experience as a pastor?"

He rocked back in his chair, placing his fingertips together over his chest. "Hm, let me think. I suppose it was the family who had a child disappear, abducted we think and never found.

"The parents were devastated, constantly fearful they would lose another of their four remaining children. The mother wouldn't let the children out of her sight, and the father virtually abandoned his family, searching day and night for his missing child. I doubt he ever stopped looking. All the kids were terrified. The eight-year-old told me he thought his sister had evaporated. An older boy said, 'evaporation' happens all the time. It can happen to anyone. He asked me if it was true. It was a tragic situation.

"I hit a wall with that family. I did my best to comfort and support them, but nothing I offered seemed to soothe their loss."

"How did you feel?" I persisted.

His reply was sudden and angry. "Like I'd failed them, of course! I felt powerless."

His sharp reaction surprised me, as if he judged me stupid or dense. The pastor glared at me. I waited as his anger slowly burned off and his eyes softened.

Holding his hands up in a helpless gesture, he admitted, "It was one of the few times in my ministry when, no matter how many hours I spent searching the scriptures, I came up empty. I could find no way to justify the sudden disappearance of a child. I couldn't find any comfort."

His hands dropped into his lap, curling up like dried leaves. Powerful hands, capable of blessing thousands of congregants every Sunday morning, allowing them to feel sacred for at least one hour each week. On this Monday morning, those same hands appeared frail and worn. He looked vulnerable and defeated. His chin hung over his chest, and he stared at the floor in silence.

I let him be for a few moments and then commented, "Fear

can be a tricky beast. I've seen many flavors of it in clients over the years. I usually ask them to consider the original purpose of fear."

He raised his head. "Say more."

"I believe we were given fear for all the right reasons but have largely forgotten its original purpose. Think of it as a survival instinct, a tool to keep us alert, and therefore alive. When ancient hunters felt fear—when the hairs went up on the backs of their arms —they knew it meant to pay attention. Today, for many people, it causes them to stop or become paralyzed. A paralyzed hunter quickly becomes prey. However, the hunter who is able to recognize fear as a signal meant to alert him to pay attention? He has a better chance of surviving."

"That's really good." He brightened. "Mind if I use that in my Sunday sermon?"

"Feel free," I answered. Suddenly he was the most animated I had seen.

"Give me a moment to make some notes," he said. Turning to his desk, he scribbled furiously on a yellow legal pad. "The topic for next Sunday is about instinctual behaviors and the discipline required to live a life congruent with the teachings of Jesus. This fear thing is a gem. Where did you find it?"

"What do you mean?" "Where did you find it? What book? I'd like to read more." "No book, just my own understanding, I began looking at fear differently when I was in Africa. I watched the native hunters and how they used their fear as an early warning system. They were aware of animals in the bush long before I was. I felt fear but was rarely certain what it was telling me. I began to listen to what fear was telling me—mostly, pay attention! If I turned on all my radar, I was more aware and confident.

It went easier with Pastor Svendahl after this exchange. It seemed I had gained some credibility.

He stepped away from the authority role often adopted by powerful clergy, and we connected man to man.

We chatted about his sermon, and he shared that writing them was something he really enjoyed. A mutual love of writing gave us additional common ground. His take on writing was that he felt closest to Jesus when he had a bible open in front of him and a pen in his hand. He pulled a worn leather box from his desk drawer and proudly showed me a beautiful old fountain pen. Every sermon he had ever delivered had been written with that pen. His father had given it to him forty-seven years before as an ordination gift.

"Often when I'm composing a sermon, I feel my father's hand on my shoulder and Jesus guiding me to the relevant passage in the Bible," he revealed. "The sacred space I spoke of earlier? I feel it when I write. I believe Jesus and my father help shape the exact message the congregation has come to hear."

"How has being a pastor all these years benefited your life?" I asked.

"Oh, countless ways. I feel privileged to be a pastor." He smiled. "Probably the most rewarding is how many people know me. My friends tease me about being the mayor of the city. Whenever we go to a restaurant or bar, people constantly come up to say hello or shake my hand. I find it gratifying that thousands of people in town know who I am."

It seemed a shame to cut our conversation short just as he had begun to open up, but I knew he had another appointment and didn't want to take more of his time. I said goodbye and assured him I could find my way out. Struck by how empty and silent the huge building was, I wandered, hoping to find the old chapel. The custodian I noticed earlier was busy washing a bank of windows in the stairwell. I asked him for directions, and he guided me through the maze of hallways.

"Can I ask you a question?" he asked.

"Certainly," I answered.

"Is your name really Snake?"

"Yes."

"Awesome, dude. I never met anyone named Snake. Hey, want to see something?"

"Sure." I guessed he was going to show me a secret passageway or a hidden altar few congregants knew existed.

He set down his squeegee and rag and looked cautiously up and down the corridor. He pulled his work shirt up to his armpits, displaying a large snake tattoo wound three times around his stomach and ending in a big, fang-filled snake's head centered on his chest. It was finely executed, a wonderful example of body art.

"It's beautiful. Where did you get it?" I asked.

"Thailand. I was surfing through Asia and found the most incredible artist." he said excitedly. He scanned the corridor again and said, "Check it out."

Suddenly he pirouetted like a ballerina, with his arms and shirt held up over his head. The snake appeared to spiral around his torso as he twirled. The effect was stunning.

"Amazing. I've never seen anything like it."

The custodian beamed with pride. Dizzy after his performance, he grasped the banister, steadying himself. "I knew you'd appreciate it. I never showed it to anyone here at work. Nice people, but I don't think they'd get it, you know?"

"I get it," I answered. "The whole Garden of Eden thing and all."

"Exactly." "You know how to get to the chapel?" he asked.

"Yeah, no problem. How lost could I get, right?"

"Right. Check out the stained glass in the chapel. It's trippy this time of the morning. The sun comes right through Jesus's flock, and the colors light up the floor."

"I will. Beautiful art. Thanks for showing me your tattoo."

"No problem, dude. Good to meet you." He went back to

sloshing soapy water on the glass and scraping it off with his squeegee.

I found my way to the chapel, and it was spectacular. Massive stone gothic pillars supported an enormous canopy of rough-hewn beams over rows of pews with seating for five thousand people. The real gem was the stained-glass rosette embedded in the wall behind the giant bronze cross, hovering over the altar. Just as the custodian had promised, the morning sunlight streamed through the deep blue and crimson stained glass, splashing brilliant light across the entire front of the chapel. I slid into a pew and looked up in rapture.

The rosette behind the altar showed Jesus holding a shepherd's staff and a flock of sheep clustered around the hem of his robe. A long line of sheep trailed off into the background, apparently following him of their own free will.

Jesus's stained glass robe and flock of sheep were impossibly white, and the many shades of green glass made the meadow they were crossing appear to be waving gently in the breeze. The custodian had been right. It was trippy. I was mesmerized.

The chapel contained the same touchstones as the church I'd attended as a child. Lectern and altar draped in heavy cotton cloth expertly embroidered with symbols of the holy trinity, doves, and the cross, the latter a dominant symbol in the chapel and a persistent reminder of Jesus's sacrifice.

Snake Bloomstrand

I was confirmed in a chapel much like this fifty years ago and felt like a member of the flock. I drifted away, the peace of mind offered by the sacrifice of a benevolent shepherd and promise of life everlasting gave way to questions that faith wouldn't satisfy.

Cooper's Hawk

A Cooper's Hawk had lunch in my backyard. He gave me a stern look as I approached. "Don't you dare, I don't share." The hawk had no need of words. The shredded pigeon and his piercing eyes convinced me he was serious.

The hawk was magnificent, mature, wise and strong in his wildness. There was little confusion in his mind. Predator or prey? No confusion for the pigeon either. His life ended at lunchtime.

Unexpectedly confronted with the predator/prey instinct crucial to all living creatures, yet so easily avoided in modern life. I felt wild for a moment, combined with a rush of fear and excitement brought on by eye contact with a powerful raptor. Perhaps my reaction was little more than an ancient survival instinct?

Despite the evolved species status we claim as "modern humans," we remain predators or prey. Perspective comes from a chance encounter with a creature walking its talk and reminds me I often forget my predator ways.

Humans are clever beasts, but we hide the messy endings that confirm our predator ways and conveniently forget we are little different from the hawk. The hawk covers his kill with a wing while we cover ours with a credit card and drive home from the grocery with a roasted chicken in a cardboard box.

A predator that neglects nature and denies reality becomes prey.

The Old Soldier

My grandmother took us picnicking in the old graveyard where generations of our family are buried. She'd gather her grandchildren in a big green Chrysler, drive through the ornate iron-gate, and park on the grass next to the lake. We'd fill tiny Dixie cups with lemonade from an old dented thermos and eat ham sandwiches while told stories and introduced us to our family. Today when I sit in the shade of those old stones I can still hear her voice.

I didn't plan on visiting my parent's gravesite today. I was running errands near the Veteran's cemetery where Mom and Dad are buried and decided to stop and clean the troublesome weeds off their tombstones. I visit every so often and have a silent chat with them.

The Veterans cemetery is massive. Identical white headstones blanket well over 450 acres. My first stop is the chapel to print out a map with the plot numbers. Twenty years, and infrequent visits, and I still get lost, searching row S for graves that have always been in row P. A map makes everything simpler.

The chapel is a magnificent example of 1940s WPA splendor. The center of the building is circular, with long stone wings stretching north and south. Limestone panels line the front of the building and pay somber tribute to each branch of the military. Skilled masons carved the scenes deeply into the flawless slabs of pinkish-orange stone.

Thick glass doors trimmed in stainless steel open into a large central room, where floor to ceiling windows offer a view of 170,000 identical white headstones. It's sobering to step through those doors and suddenly be confronted with this slumbering carpet of marble.

Years ago retired veterans wrestled with the big leather-bound ledgers stored in the records room. They would page through the enormous books, run one finger down the alphabetical list, and scrawl a plot number on a strip of paper. If you were polite and respectful, they might even point in the general direction of the grave you were seeking.

Most of the building is blocked off to the public now. The records room and old veterans are gone, and a stainless-steel box slightly larger than a man sits in front of the windows, offering a touch screen. You simply punch a name, and the gravesite location is displayed. Push Print and a detailed map drops into a tray. It's far more efficient, but I miss the gruff retired soldiers.

An old man stood in front of the printer this afternoon, punching the big simulated buttons displayed on the screen. He had a long list of names in one hand and a pen in the other, and was obviously struggling to type and write simultaneously.

The sides of the machine were the only flat writing surfaces in the room, and it appeared he could use an extra arm. Flustered, he peeled his paper off the screen and stepped aside. "Go ahead. I've got lots of names to find."

"I'm in no hurry," I replied, "Would you like some help?"

"I could use some." He said with a warm smile. "Would you write down the plot numbers while I type in the names?"

"I'd be glad to." I called out the first name scrawled on the list. "Pierson."

He carefully typed it, gave the machine a minute, and then repeated the name adding the plot location. "Pierson, row *K*, plot 2189."

I settled on the floor. At a glance, it looked like over twenty handwritten names on the list. We quickly fell into a rhythm, and began to chat between entries.

"I worked at the airport across the street until I retired. I used to power-walk in the cemetery during lunch with a beautiful woman. She looked just like Olivia Newton John in the movie Grease." He winked at me. "I never married," he admitted, "Been a bachelor all my life. The shop supervisors loved me. No wife or family, so I could work all the overtime they could dish out. I came back from Korea in 1953 and was working within two weeks. I worked on planes for forty-three years! What's the next name?"

"Swansen, with an *E*."

"Yeah, I remember him, Pete Swansen. He was in artillery," the old man reminisced. "We used to play poker together. If I remember right, he died at the Battle of the Hook, shot by a rogue sniper as he helped load a howitzer. Killed instantly."

He punched the letters in one at a time. "I remember seeing piles of shell casings from those howitzers. Piled ten feet high and lining the road for a quarter of a mile. Those artillerymen threw a lot of lead over the thirty-eighth parallel. Swansen, Peter, row *L*, plot 3387. Next?"

"Toomey, John."

"Spell Toomey for me."

I did so.

"John lost one foot and all his toes to frostbite at the Chosin Reservoir. He made it home, but he was crippled and could hardly use his hands after they'd been frozen so badly, but he lived until 1987. John Toomey, row *B*, plot 1902. Next!"

We worked our way down the list. He had a story to go along with each soldier's name. "There are twenty-two names listed here. Why are you doing this?" I asked.

"This weekend is the fourth of July, and you won't be able to get near this machine. People will be lined up out the door waiting for maps. I'm getting a jump on them." He smiled obviously proud of his strategy.

"No," I clarified. "Why so many names?"

He looked at me like I was dense. "They were my friends," he replied matter-of-factly. "I visit them every Fourth of July. I met them all in Korea. We went through hell. We fought together, ate together, and slept together. Half of the men on that list never made it home, and the remaining died over the years, one after another."

He shuffled over to the window and stood with his back to me, looking out across the rolling landscape and the stone markers, standing sentry. His crooked body straightened to attention as he removed a worn field cap with **Korean Veteran** embroidered across the brim. He held the cap over his heart with one hand and raised the other to his forehead in a crisp salute. I sat on the floor, mesmerized. The old soldier saluting against the backdrop of soldier's graves was a heartbreaking image.

He spoke in a shaky voice. "They're family, my family."

The room suddenly filled with a humbling sense of honor and respect.

"It might surprise you," he said; back still turned, "to know I started visiting here right after the war. It often took months for the bodies to arrive. I've been visiting for almost sixty years. Ate my lunch here most days. In my forties, I even joined the Honor Guard. We offered a rifle salute to any soldier whose family wanted it. Some didn't. The sound of rifle shots upset some people. Me? I think it's the most fitting tribute for a soldier.

"I used to remember all the grave locations, and I'd have lunch at a different one each day. Now I have to ask a machine and get help from a kind stranger."

"Glad to help," I answered.

He put the cap back on his freckled bald head and moved over in front of the screen. "What's the next name?" he asked solemnly.

"Feldman, Morris Feldman." He punched letters and muttered under his breath, "Getting old isn't easy, you know. A man ends up with way too much time to think."

"I can imagine." "Morris Feldman, row *B*, plot 7326. One left?" he asked.

I finished writing and read the last name to him. "Sam Wellik." I could tell the name landed hard on the old man's memory.

"Sam," he repeated, pausing as he reached toward the keypad and grasping the stainless-steel lip of the large box instead. He seemed to be holding on for dear life. "Are you okay?" I asked, fearful he was having a heart attack.

He gave me a sharp look and began to type. He stopped mid-point and looked me square in the eye. "I sure remember how to spell Sam's name," he admonished. "I can still see it stenciled on his uniform. We were good friends. Went on patrol together and spent countless nights wide awake in the dark and scared. He was one of the most courageous men I've ever known.

"When I was shot, Sam wouldn't leave my side. The bullet that hit me went in my chest and collapsed one of my lungs. I couldn't breathe, and I panicked. Sam held his hand over the hole in my chest, and I could breathe a little. Damn, I was terrified!" The old man stared through me as he spoke, completely adrift in battlefield memories. "I'm sure it didn't take long for the medic to reach us, but it felt like hours," he continued. "I lay on the ground, struggling to breathe and looking up at Wellik printed above his pocket. Sam kept his hand on my chest, shouting 'Medic' over and over. After they arrived he stayed, guarding us.

"Last time I saw him was when they loaded my stretcher in the basket outside the helicopter. The blades threw dirt in my face as they covered me with a blanket and strapped me in. I grabbed Sam's hand and said thank you." He shuddered. "Never did see Sam again. Later, when I was recovering in the hospital, a buddy came to visit and told me Sam had gone back on patrol and was killed that same day.

"I accidentally discovered he was buried here. I knew he was from the area, but I had never thought to look. I found his grave in the early '70s and even visited his brother. Told him how Sam saved my life. He was twenty when he died. It was 1952. I've eaten a lot of bag lunches next to Sam's grave."

He punched in the rest of the letters. The screen went blank for a second and retrieved the data. "Sam Wellik, row *T,* plot 3313."

I wrote them on the list. "Last one," I announced. "All finished."

He was staring at the screen like he'd seen a ghost and suddenly swore in an angry, loud voice, "Goddamn it!" He slammed his hand down on the thick glass screen, startling me.

"Damn it!" he shouted again, his words echoing around the empty room.

"What's wrong?" "They've screwed up his service records. Look! They have the wrong dates." He took a step back and pointed at the screen, furious eyes blazing under bushy gray eyebrows. "Look!" I stood slowly, stiff from squatting on the floor. I grabbed the sheet of paper and coaxed my old legs to straighten.

I read the data on the screen.

"See?" he shouted. "They got his birth and death dates right, but his service dates are off by ten years. It pisses me off when that happens. Some bored data entry person at the VA entered in the wrong numbers. Give me that paper."

He snatched the list out of my hand and copied the incorrect service dates into the margin. "I'm mad as hell! The man gave his life for his country. Least they can do is get the dates right." He glared at me.

The old man shook the paper and slammed the side of the machine, punctuating his words with sharp slaps to the metal skin of the computer. "I'm going over to the VA right now. I have to fix this! I'll find out who enters this stuff and set them straight, I have to go. Thanks for your help I appreciate it." He held out his hand. We shook, and then he said, "They close at 4:30. I have to get this fixed today." As he headed for the door, I called after him, "Wait!"

He stopped just inside the door.

"What's your name?" I asked.

"Henry. Henry Shaddegg" he answered, and a sly smile crossed his face as he added, "Row *T*, plot 3314." He grinned at the shock on my face. "No." he said, "I'm no ghost. I reserved the plot next to Sam. I have no family, so I figured I'd handle my own affairs. Who else is there to do it? I even set up the honor guard. Eight rifles. Usually we fire three volleys, but at my funeral they will do four. Figured I'd add one for Sam."

"Proud to meet you, Henry Shaddegg." I stood at attention and saluted him. He returned it, saying, "I have to go, one more mission, thanks again for your help." He whirled and strode out the door. He looked twenty years younger than when I'd first seen him, struggling with the info box. Remarkable what a mission does for a man, regardless of age.

I punched my last name in, and my father's name popped onto the screen. Row *P*, plot 2912. I pushed the big blue print button and listened to the mechanism wave ink over a sheet of paper. The machine slowly spit the map from a slot and dropped it in the tray.

I sat with Mom and Dad for a bit. I pulled a few weeds, then took a knife from the toolkit in my truck and used it to edge the grass neatly around the gravestones. Dad always liked the lawn neatly edged. I always feel tenderhearted when I read the epitaph on my mother's headstone: Our beloved teacher. She wasn't formally a teacher, but she did teach everyone who knew her about compassion, integrity, wisdom, and so many other important life-skills.

I didn't stay long; the July sun was blazing. I was grateful the big sprinklers were shooting staccato jets of water sixty feet in all directions. The mist cooled me down as I cut the sod with my knife. I got back in my truck soaking wet.

I flipped on the radio as I drove home and caught the tail end of a program. Two authors were being interviewed, one a young Iraq war vet, the other an older Vietnam veteran. Each had written memoirs based on their combat experience.

The interviewer asked the older veteran, "Would you recommend young people join the military?"

After a long pause, he answered. "No, I wouldn't. Don't get me wrong. I'm proud of my service. I grew into a man when I decided to serve my country. It was the first truly selfless act I ever did in my life. The men and women I served with became like family to me. But the cost is like a maxed-out credit card. The interest will kill you.

"Combat leaves a mark on a soldier, a mark that never fades and never, ever goes away. Combat veterans carry this burden silently their entire lives." He went further. "We go to war impetuously. Most Americans don't realize what's involved. The consequences of war are far too serious. A war might end for politicians and citizens, but it never ends for the soldiers or its victims. The burden is a heavy lift over a lifetime."

I clicked off the radio, thinking about my chance encounter with Henry that July afternoon. The air-conditioned cab felt wonderful after being in the hot sun. I turned the fan up, and as the cold air hit my wet clothes, goose bumps raised the hairs on both my arms. A deep chill whistled through my bones as my mother's epitaph came to mind.

"Our beloved teacher."

Today an unexpected teacher had offered me two lessons. One, about the commitment we make to the memory of those we love, the other a much harder lesson, clearly revealing the true weight of those memories.

I guess my grandma was familiar with both lessons, gathering her flock of ducklings together in the big old Chrysler and using her stories to introduce her grandchildren to a long-buried family. I will always carry a bag of her stories near my heart. Never a burden, they explained where I came from.

I parked in my driveway, searched my truck for a pen, and scribbled, "Henry Shadegg, Row *T*, plot 3314," on the map I'd printed earlier. I slipped the folded sheet of paper between the maps and manuals jammed in my glove box.

I resisted opening the door and facing the blast of heat outside, replaying the afternoon in my head, grateful for my accidental meeting with the old soldier.

I must remember to have lunch with Henry sometime in the future.

Say Goodbye

Simon and I reluctantly joined the same tribe, the "Cancer Tribe." Inhabiting bodies friendly to cancer, and willing to tell the unvarnished truth, we found comfort speaking honestly with one another.

Simon had been diagnosed with an extraordinarily complex cancer. He'd endured four years of surgeries, medications, and treatments. In spite of long hospital stays, and eating his meals through a tube for over a year, he'd discovered the ability to face cancer with determination, courage, and an inquisitive heart. Now his emotional reserves were swiftly evaporating.

I'd dodged a bullet. My cancer was in remission. That's the word doctors use when complete recovery will remain forever elusive. A body can fully recover from a broken leg, but a cancer diagnosis leads survivors to look over their shoulder for a lifetime.

As cancer rudely attacked our bodies, heartbreaking challenges ran through our lives. At our most vulnerable and unreliable, we were forced to navigate financial ruin, stressed and exhausted spouses, children so full of grief they could only show anger, and lifelong friends suddenly too fearful to even pick up the phone.

Simon and I ignored social etiquette. We placed a high value on candor and had grown very thick skins. We tackled topics far too edgy for polite company. After rambling through an update on treatments recommended by doctors, or commiserating over side effects and recent test results, we'd drop down low and peer into life's bottomless bucket of unfinished business.

"We've been asking the wrong question," Simon announced when I arrived for a visit. Never a man to squander words, he spoke abruptly and to the point.

"What question?" I asked.

"The no more question," he replied. "What will finally convince us to say no more treatment? When might we throw in the towel and surrender?" We'd speculated during a recent conversation what would be the final straw.

I urged him to continue.

"It's been troubling me since we last spoke. A choice based on how much I can endure feels far too passive. I woke a couple of days ago with a different question: 'Am I ready to say goodbye?'"

Simon watched my face as his re-frame washed over me. Suddenly the decision to persevere felt within my control and not simply a reaction to pain and suffering or a doctor's opinion. Am I ready to say goodbye?

"A far better question," I responded, "Do you have an answer?"

He stared out the window for a moment. "Yes I do. I called hospice this morning, I'm refusing further treatment and beginning to say my goodbyes."

Simon explained how he'd arrived at this decision. His cancer was spreading. One more lengthy hospitalization would wipe out his savings, along with any equity left in his home. Simon's wife, Olivia, was exhausted and stretched to the limit, caring for him. Simon had a long list of "hard data" influencing his decision, including the fact that his pain was increasing to a degree that large doses of medication were required just to blunt the edge. He was fearful the drugs would cloud his mind completely soon.

"I want to say my goodbye while I'm still clear-headed," he confessed. "I spoke with Olivia yesterday. First she got angry and called me a quitter, and then she cried and made me promise to save my last goodbye for her. I expect I'll be able to make good on that. I can't imagine anyone I'd rather be with when I draw my last breath. She's a good woman, and I love her dearly. In the meantime, I intend to get down to business."

"How do you plan to accomplish this?" I asked.

"I figured I'd begin with all the things that piss me off and work my way up to everything I love. Kind of like climbing a ladder, the low rungs are easy, but I cling tight to the ones at the top." He laughed, clearly entertained by his own dark humor.

"Clever," I replied, rolling my eyes. Once he'd thoroughly enjoyed the joke, I pressed him for an answer. "Seriously, how will you do this?"

As if suddenly inspired, he said, "Here, I'll show you." He rummaged through the collection of pill bottles in the nightstand drawer and pulled out a tarnished silver pocket watch. He held it up to his ear, shook it, listened again, and said, "Help me sit up."

He cradled the watch in his hands while I propped him upright with pillows. He looked ancient and frail. Years of chemo and radiation had winnowed him down to skin and bones. He slowly wound the mainspring twenty-four times, one for every hour, no more, no less, counting aloud as he did so. He opened the face, set the hands to the proper time, and held it up to his ear again.

He smiled. "My father was killed in a mining accident when I was nine years old. He went off to work one morning and never came home. I was sitting on the porch a couple of days later when one of his friends showed up at the house to offer condolences. The man reached into his coat pocket, pulled out a red handkerchief, and handed it to me, saying, 'this was your father's. Now you should have it.' This very watch was wrapped inside the handkerchief." Simon held it up for me to see. "I've kept it nearby all these years. I never polished it, the case still has my father's fingerprints on the surface." He cupped it in his palm, tracing the fingerprints with one bony finger.

"Have you ever had someone you love unexpectedly vanish?" he asked without looking up. "It leaves an incomplete feeling, like a book missing the last few pages. I imagine that is why saying goodbye feels so important to me right now." Simon offered the watch to me. "Here, hold it." He looked me in the eye before dropping the watch into my open hand. "I want you to have it. Goodbye, watch."

"Simon, I can't take your father's watch. It should go to one of your kids," I protested, thinking an intimate family touchstone like this should stay in his family.

He wouldn't take it back. "It's yours now. You asked me a question, and this is my answer."

"Question?"

"How will I say my goodbyes?" Simon said. "This is exactly how I'll do it. I'll say them one at a time. Goodbye to my books, tools, and trinkets. Goodbye to my garden and the creek that runs behind my house. I'll say goodbye to my friends and my children, and lastly I'll kiss my wife goodbye. Drugs and pain won't steal the last few pages of my story. I'll say my goodbyes now."

My conversations with Simon were beautiful. After years of gathering life close, we spoke of release, of letting go of what we'd found precious. We seldom spoke of loss, choosing instead to talk of love. Man or woman, we all reach a moment when we must say goodbye to everything. Simon showed me the beauty in saying goodbye and how important it is to close the door when we leave.

Solitary Men

Solitary men keep secrets. They walk through life alone, silently adhering to a routine of predictable days shaped with thick, calloused hands. Fate or choice presents them with a very different life than the familiar script followed by many men. They have no wife or children and few friends.

If lucky they live on the outskirts of another man's family. If not, they live alone in small one-room apartments or isolated old farmhouses with Spartan decor and cupboards stocked with simple food.

Married men secretly admire solitary men and romanticize what it might be like to live a life responsible only to oneself. The fantasy evaporates when they consider the promise of long lonely years.

It remains a mystery why some men choose a solitary life. Luck and circumstance, apply a heavy hand on the shaping of a life. When asked the all too familiar question, "Why didn't you marry?" their response is often, "Never met the right woman." But a deeper truth lies beneath their casual response. Some were hurt early, causing them to never trust again. Others were simply shy and uncertain, unable or unwilling to share the quiet blanket under which they sleep.

Uncle Martin, my grandfather's brother, was one of these solitary men. A lifelong bachelor, Martin made his home for decades on the edge of my grandfather's family.

The brothers were born on a small flat outcropping of stone perched high above one of Norway's most beautiful fjords. The stunning landscape is hopelessly rocky and near vertical. A thirty-foot-square cabin with a slate roof somehow sheltered the family of seven boys and their parents. Apple trees and potatoes were among the few crops grown, and fish was a staple. Custom dictated the eldest son would inherit the small plot of land, and the remaining six brothers were forced to make their own way in the world.

Grandfather and Martin emigrated to America, settling first in North Dakota, then permanently in Minnesota, where flat land and opportunity promised a bright future.

Martin learned a trade and became a boiler man, working his

entire life in the dark cellars of giant buildings. His work world was a noisy place built of steel, and full of steam pipes and coal fire.

Grandpa found work with the railroad, first as a laborer and then as a skilled carpenter, lining rail cars with wood or building small town train stations across the Red River Valley. It was during his travels that he met my grandmother. She worked as a cook, feeding the many men who wandered far from home building railroads, clearing land, or harvesting crops.

Grandpa was the only brother who ever married. Maybe growing up in a tiny cabin convinced the other six brothers a solitary life was a luxury. Maybe Grandma was tenacious enough to beat down any resistance Grandpa might have showed, maybe it was her cooking, or most likely they just loved one another. She was undeniably a force of nature and more than capable of filling the lives of the two silent brothers with drama, gossip, and endless opinions on a wide range of topics.

Each evening a river of fresh bread, roast chicken, and potatoes baked in her kitchen while "the men" sat in the parlor, reading their two preferred forms of literature: the newspaper or the Bible. The fact that little but silence ever came from the parlor never inhibited Grandma. One-way conversation was good enough for her. The two men worked, read, ate, and slept. Cooking and speaking remained her domain.

She would pick a topic or a target and talk tirelessly in the general direction of her mute audience, sharing her thoughts and judgments generously. The men never seemed troubled by her rants, except on the rare occasion when they found themselves the target of her harsh judgments. They would remain silent until her words pushed past some invisible line, at which point Grandpa would pull out the silver bullet. Tremors would begin deep in his chest, his normally soft voice would rumble in a low growl, and two words would burst from his mouth: "Hush, woman."

The house would instantly go silent, the men would resume reading, and the ticking clock or a stew pot bubbling on the range would be the only sounds heard for an hour or two. The three of them made an odd trio. Both men loved Grandma. "Hush, woman" was never used with disrespect but only used as a line drawn in the sand between two stone-silent men and a woman with a bucket full of opinions.

Eventually Grandma would begin again, ramping up slowly with a non-controversial topic. Her harsh judgments of Cousin Mabel tended to be a safe bet. All three agreed Mabel had earned the most critical words.

Uncle Martin and Grandpa spent the early evening in the parlor, each seated in a favorite chair, keeping up with their reading while Grandma bustled about in the kitchen. All three ate meals together, but Martin spent much of his free time in his room, perched on the edge of his bed playing solitaire. Martin found silent pleasure in the game after dinner or on his days off and could usually be found alone in his room with a deck of cards, dressed in one of three white shirts, a tie, arm garters, and wool trousers, no matter what the temperature. The only sounds that came from his room were the whisper of shuffled cards and the ticking of his wind-up alarm clock.

Grandma had a reputation for interfering in people's lives. Convinced she knew what was best for everyone, she dispensed advice generously. She also considered herself an accomplished doctor and prescribed horrific home remedies aimed at fixing any ailment. Cook, doctor, psychologist—growing up on the Great Plains, a woman had to wear many hats.

She kept a miracle cure in a pint bottle on a shelf. Hard to say how old the bottle was. The yellowed label had a picture of a running horse above a printed list of ailments the contents were guaranteed to cure. It referred to "maladies" suffered by the human body, and the instructions explained the "medicine" could be taken by the spoonful or used as a liniment rubbed liberally on the hide of a horse to heal weeping sores and punctures. I never saw her actually uncork the bottle. All she had to do was wave it about, and the suffering patient instantly recovered. It was miraculous!

Most people had the good sense to avoid Grandma's doctoring. However, it was impossible to avoid her meddling in people's lives. Once she set her mind to fixing a broken life, little short of an unexpected death could distract her.

When Martin reached his 40s, still unmarried, she figured his life needed fixing. Martin was happy and content alone, but she set out on a mission. She decided it was time for him to find a good woman. She laid out a powerful case for marriage, using all her persuasive powers, aimed at convincing him his life would be wasted without a woman at his side.

He patiently listened to her arguments during dinner night after night. Every evening ended with Martin silently getting up from the table, walking to his room, settling on the edge of his bed, and shuffling his cards.

Failing to enlist his enthusiasm, grandma took matters into her own hands. She interviewed women she felt would be a suitable match. She trolled the market and church for widows or single women interested in marriage and invited many of them to Sunday dinner, displaying them for Martin's benefit. The candidates spent the meal unsuccessfully trying to get Martin to speak. His silence remained impenetrable. One by one they surrendered, retreating into a conversation with Grandma. Martin would sit politely until the women's gossip was well under way, wait for his opportunity, then slip quietly from the table and head for his room.

Martin was a decent-looking man, a hard worker, polite. He made good money, didn't drink, and only occasionally smoked a pipe. When word got around that he was available, his solitary life became a nightmare. Grandma booked invitations to Sunday dinner a month in advance.

Martin's habit, of going for a leisurely walk alone after church on Sunday came to an end after Lenore Aase ambushed him. She was waiting next to Pastor Olson as he left church. Martin shook hands with the pastor, and before he could escape, Lenore firmly linked arms with him and asked if he would walk her home. Martin looked to the pastor for redemption, but Pastor Olson knew what the poor man was up against and could only offer a compassionate shrug.

Lenore led Martin away from the chapel with a firm hand, chattering away, determined to crack the silence for which he was becoming infamous. She was unsuccessful. He walked her home, said goodbye, and beat a hasty retreat.

Martin quit sitting with Grandma and Grandpa in the front pew of the chapel, choosing instead a seat in the very last row on the aisle and bolting out the door as soon as Pastor Olson uttered the benediction.

Undaunted by Martin's reluctance, word quickly spread among the women, and they eagerly joined Grandma in her mission. Any woman successful at finally cornering him would certainly become a local hero. Somehow, someway, Martin's bachelor lifestyle was going to end. The women would see to it.

The men looked on Martin with compassion, and the wise

ones knew better than to interfere. Palmer Johansson came home drunk one night and foolishly lectured his wife, "You women should just leave Martin alone. Maybe he doesn't want to get married."

Palmer ended up sleeping under an old moldy blanket on the front porch that night, sending a clear message to all the men. Martin was in serious trouble.

The men rallied around Martin, out of earshot of the women, offering words of sympathetic support. They gave him cover as best they could, but there was little to be done. He had a target on his back, and no shield would change that fact. If he'd been a drinker, he could have taken up residence at the nearby tavern, but he wasn't. The drunken chatter at the local tavern didn't appeal to Martin any more than polite Sunday dinner conversation at home with Grandma's candidates. He wasn't just silent around women. He never had much to say around men either.

Silent men make women crazy. Women need details. All laid out on the table, details provide a sense of safety. A woman may sort through them repeatedly in an earnest effort to understand or make a critical choice. Men tend to feel overwhelmed or depressed if too much is placed in front of them at any given time. Men appreciate bite-sized pieces.

Men aren't troubled by silence in the same way. Friendship and acceptance are easily found without many words. Grandpa and Martin enjoyed fishing and would take their gear down to the river on summer afternoons, hoping for a stringer of bluegills. Hours would pass without a full sentence. They had a language all their own, built on a solid foundation of two words: ya or nay.

Beyond that, what more needs to be said?

If an especially large fish was reeled in, they might congratulate one another with, "Ya, dat's a good von." This many words strung together were rare and only used in moments of extreme excitement. A slight smile and a pleasant grunt of satisfaction was enough to convey that all was well and affirm they were thoroughly enjoying themselves.

It was at the end of one of these fishing afternoons that Lenore escalated the hunt. She and Grandma hatched a plan after church and laid a trap for Martin. Lenore was waiting for the two men when they returned home from the river. Seated on the porch, and still wearing her Sunday dress, she stood as they cautiously came up the steps. "Julia was called away to help at church. She asked if I would start dinner for you. Let me take those fish. You go wash up. Dinner will be ready shortly."

Lenore snatched the stringer of fish and headed for the backyard, leaving Martin and Grandpa standing on the porch empty-handed and uneasy. The shock was almost more than they could bear. No woman but Grandma ever cooked in her kitchen. They understood the women had upped the ante, yet they were powerless. Their pleasant afternoon of fishing had taken a nasty turn. There was little to be done now, but see where this would lead.

They washed up and bolted for their parlor sanctuary, settling nervously into chairs and hiding their faces behind sections of the Sunday newspaper while Lenore bustled about in Grandma's kitchen, rattling pans and frying bluegills. Right on cue Grandma walked in, just in time to set out plates and call the men to the table.

Lenore set the large platter of fish in the center of the table. Grandma thanked Lenore for helping out, and turned to the men with a serious look. "Wasn't it nice of Lenore to cook dinner?"

They knew Grandma meant business, and both offered a few genuine words of gratitude while Lenore beamed with pride. They loaded their plates as the women traded expertise on the fine details of frying fish, which was delicious, Grandma spent most of the meal praising the cook and trying to pry compliments from the men. Lenore was to be the center of attention and a simple ya or nay wasn't going to pass muster.

She forced them to explain exactly where they caught the fish, the bait they used, and how their mother had cooked it. Grandma aimed to get complete sentences out of them and include Lenore in the conversation. It was like watching her pull rusty nails from an old board with her teeth.

As the platter emptied, the women got serious.

"How can I ever repay you?" Grandma asked.

"Oh, no need. I enjoy cooking for people who appreciate

good food. It's no fun cooking for myself. I so wish I had someone to cook for once in a while," Lenore replied, her eyes boring into Martin's skull.

He kept his eyes down, meticulously wiping his plate with a slice of bread. His plate was gleaming, and nobody spoke as the two women waited expectantly for him to respond to this hint. He knew Lenore was offering an invitation.

He reached for his napkin, spent a few minutes carefully wiping his chin, folded the napkin carefully, and set it down gently next to his plate.

Silence. He wasn't going to take the bait.

Lenore could see polite hints were going nowhere, so she got right to the point. "Martin, would you come to my house next Friday for dinner?"

He looked to his brother for help, but Grandpa was wisely staying out of this. He was caught in the trap. Grandpa reached for the last piece of fish, avoiding eye contact with his brother. Martin looked hopefully in Grandma's direction.

She was more than happy to help him out. "Why, Lenore, how generous. I'm sure Martin would love to have dinner with you."

Both women wore a look of grim determination. There was no graceful way out. Martin's lower lip trembled slightly. "I'd be grateful, Lenore."

The women worked out the details as he sat silently in his

chair. His fate was now completely in their hands. As they cleared the table, Martin said, "Thank you," excused himself, went into his room, and closed the door.

Grandma and Lenore were giddy as they straightened the kitchen. They had finally won a major victory in their war against silent men. They settled on a time and consulted on Martin's favorite food. As Lenore put on her coat to leave, Grandma whispered, "Martin will be there if I have to drag him by the ear."

The week passed quickly, and word spread through the neighborhood. Martin and Lenore would have dinner together on Friday night. A couple of men tried to commiserate with Martin, but as usual he had little to say. They looked on him with pity, understanding the hopelessness of his situation. The women were all abuzz, gossiping back and forth and speculating on what would come next. Lenore became a celebrity among the women, her tenacity seen as a virtue.

Martin went about his week, following his predictable routine. Wake up at 6 a.m., take the streetcar to work, home at five, read the paper, eat dinner, cards, and sleep.

Grandma couldn't help herself, prodding Martin in an attempt to get a sense of what he was thinking. "It's nice of Lenore to fix dinner for you," she said during dinner one night.

"Ya," he replied.

"What do you suppose she will cook?" Grandma said,

pushing.

Martin wasn't about to indulge her and offered only a shrug.

Friday morning Grandma laid out breakfast for the men, and just to be certain, reminded Martin, "You make sure to get right home after work. Lenore wants you at her house at six."

"Ya," he replied as he left for work.

He arrived home that afternoon to find his suit and a freshly laundered shirt neatly laid out on his bed. His Sunday shoes were polished and waiting on the floor.

Grandma was jumpy as a cat. She rushed him to clean up and shave and insisted he stand in the kitchen for inspection. "You look so handsome," she said, brushing lint off his suit and trying to get a read on what he was thinking.

They stood awkwardly in the kitchen until Grandma suggested, "I suppose you should get going."

"Ya," he replied. He hesitated for a long moment at the door, with one hand on the doorknob, then turned to Grandma and muttered one word. "Bye."

She pulled supper together while Grandpa sat alone in the parlor, reading. The house felt empty without Martin. The three of them had a routine, and although Martin wasn't the best conversationalist, they were both aware of the empty chair at the table. Grandma was quiet, preoccupied with her thoughts, wondering how Lenore and Martin were getting along. After supper, she washed the dishes, cleaned the kitchen, and suggested they go for a walk. Her nervousness had gotten the better of her, and a walk would help to pass the time.

They wandered through the neighborhood, window-shopping and visiting with neighbors, making the most of the mild summer evening, and arrived back home about 8:30. The phone was ringing as Grandpa unlocked the door. Grandma answered. It was Lenore, and she was hysterical. Martin never arrived for dinner.

Lenore was inconsolable. She had prepared a meal that had gone to waste, and she angrily made it clear she had never been treated so rudely. Grandma's attempts to apologize fell on deaf ears.

Grandpa slipped on his jacket and was headed for the door by the time she hung up. "I'll go look for him." He heard the angry rattle of pots and pans as he walked away from the house. If he did find Martin, Grandma wasn't going to go easy on him.

Martin didn't have many friends and rarely visited the local taverns, where so many of the single men spent their evenings. But Grandpa made the rounds, asking if anyone had seen him or had any idea where he might be. He worried that an accident had happened, so he stopped by the police station.

The cop at the front desk said, "No accidents. It's a quiet night. Nothing reported."

Grandpa was getting nervous. It was unlike Martin to disappear without a word. On a hunch, he went to the train station and asked the ticket seller if he had seen Martin. Sure enough, the man had sold Martin a ticket to Chicago.

"He bought a one-way ticket. I thought it was strange, so I asked if he was taking a vacation," the ticket seller remarked. "He said he was. I asked if he wanted a return ticket. He said he didn't. He left on the 7:00 train. Is anything wrong?"

Grandpa was stunned. Martin had left town without a word to anyone. As he went home to give Grandma the bad news, he couldn't believe Martin would leave town just to avoid dinner with Lenore, but it sure seemed to be the case. Why Chicago? Martin didn't know anyone there.

She didn't take the news well. "He left? What do you mean? He ran away?"

Grandpa tried to explain, but he was just as surprised by Martin's sudden disappearance, and honestly there wasn't much to explain. The pressure Grandma had put on Martin to "find a nice woman" over the past several months had been relentless. His quiet bachelor life had become a nightmare. The parade of women attending Sunday dinner seemed endless. And now her mission had gone horribly wrong.

"He ran away to avoid having dinner with Lenore?" Grandma kept repeating. "Not a word to either one of us? He's a grown man." She searched the rooms in the little house, as if she would find Martin hiding in a corner, all the time muttering, "I can't believe it."

She went into Martin's room and discovered his few clothes still hanging in the closet, his Bible and a deck of cards on the bedside table. "He didn't pack anything and left with only the clothes on his back," she shouted to Grandpa, who was sitting calmly at the kitchen table.

As her anger wound down, she joined him. "What on earth am I going to tell Lenore?" she asked.

"Tell her the truth," Grandpa replied. "He ran away."

"She will be crushed. Everyone will know he ran away rather than go to dinner," she replied.

Grandpa was a man of few words, but as the two of them sat in the darkened kitchen, he had a lot to say. "Julia, you know how shy Martin is. He never showed any interest in getting married or having a family of his own. You and all the women in the neighborhood have been pestering him for months. You decided he needed to get married. I don't agree with the fool notion he needed to run away. I'm angry he never talked to me, but you were wrong to assume he didn't know what was best for himself. Meddling in other people's lives never leads to anything good."

"She knew the truth of his words. Her meddling had caused trouble before. Although she was angry, she began to realize how reluctant Martin had been and how he had indulged her matchmaking just to make her happy. She had left him little option other than to leave. It was either that or face a steady stream of prospective wives for the rest of his life. Martin had been happy and content on his own. He was a committed bachelor and at peace with his choice.

He was a solitary man, and he would remain one.

Lenore never spoke to Grandma again, avoiding her when they crossed paths. The neighborhood gossips had all the excitement they could stand for weeks, until another drama replaced Martin's sudden disappearance.

Martin became somewhat of a folk hero among the men, playing out a fantasy family men often indulge in. Hitting the road with only the clothes on your back, free as a bird.

After a time, the gossip faded. Grandma and Grandpa occasionally spoke of him, wondering where he was or why they hadn't received a letter, letting them know he was alive. Martin had always been somewhat of a mystery. No one knew much about him, and his habitual silence added to the mystery.

Five years passed without a word from him.

One evening after supper, Grandma and Grandpa were sitting in the parlor when they heard the door open. Footsteps crossed the linoleum floor, and suddenly Martin was standing in the room, hands in the pockets of his coat and a bashful look on his face. He asked, "Am I still welcome here?"

Grandma jumped up and gave him a hug. Grandpa rose from

his chair smiling and shook his brother's hand. Martin shyly accepted their affection.

Grandma started right in. "Where have you been? We've been worried sick about you. We thought you were dead. Why didn't you write?"

Martin just shrugged.

Grandpa said, "Are you hungry? Do you want something to eat?"

"Ya," Martin replied.

Grandma bustled around the kitchen, fixing a plate for him while the two men sat in the parlor, speaking quietly.

"Do you still have a room for me?" he asked Grandpa.

"Ya, your room is just as you left it. Julia always had a feeling you'd be back," Grandpa replied.

"I stopped on my way here and got my old job back. I start tomorrow morning," Martin said.

"That's good."

Grandma called the men into the kitchen, set a plate of cold chicken, bread, and butter in front of Martin, then joined them at the table. "Just like old times, the three of us sitting down to eat."

Martin nodded.

"How's your health?" she asked.

"Good," he replied with a mouthful of chicken.

"Are you staying for a while?"

"Ya."

Grandma made small talk as Martin filled up on chicken. She offered him a piece of chocolate cake for dessert, and he gratefully dug into it. "I missed your cake, Julia," he said, smearing the last of the frosting around his plate with a fork.

"Suppose you're tired?" Grandpa asked.

"Ya," he replied. "I could use a good night's sleep." Martin stood. "Thanks for supper, Julia. Think I'll go to bed." He said goodnight and went to his room.

Grandpa cleared the table as Grandma washed and stacked dishes to dry on the drain board. She whispered, "Did he say where he's been?"

"Nay," Grandpa replied.

"Five years without a word, and he didn't say anything?"

"Well, he did say he got his job back. He starts in the morning." "That's all?" "Ya. I'm going to bed. Are you coming?"

"In a minute. I'm just going to finish the dishes."

She wiped her hands on her apron, hung it on the hook next to the cupboard, and stood, looking out the kitchen window. "What is it with these men? Why don't they speak? He disappears for five years, then walks in and acts like he's been gone for an hour."

She peered down the hallway and noticed Martin's door was open a crack. The light was on, and she could hear cards being shuffled. She cracked.

Grandma pushed the door open and stepped into the room. Martin was sitting on the edge of his bed. He looked up, and she launched into him.

"I'm so angry I could spit. We thought you were dead. You left home without a word, disappeared for five years, and suddenly show up like nothing ever happened. I ask questions, and I get no response. We were so worried about you. I've had it, Martin! Where have you been?"

Martin considered her question carefully before responding, "I went back to Norway for a bit."

Silence filled the room.

"That's it? Five years, and that's all you have to say?"

"Ya."

Grandma exploded. "I just don't understand you, Martin. You make me crazy. All the years we've known one another, and I still can't get you to talk. It's no wonder you are still a bachelor. No woman could ever live with a man with as few words as you have. You're going to be single your whole life." She stormed from the room and slammed the door.

Martin shuffled his cards and laid them out on the bed. He whispered, "Ya," and a big grin spread across his face.

The End of the Chase

A wise man placed his hand on my shoulder and offered some sage advice. "Don't try to train him. It'll just frustrate you and piss off the dog."

He was speaking of the mini-dachshund my wife had just purchased. On a Saturday visit to the pet store, she scooped the tiny puppy out of his cage and pleaded, "Can we get him?" Suddenly my wife was seven years old. Resistance was futile.

I admit a preference for large dogs. Tiny dogs don't seem as practical, but as Oscar grew, I came to admire his fifteen pounds of pure cunning. What the wiener dog lacked in size, he made up for in attitude and tenacity. We've had a difficult relationship. Any dachshund owner will confirm how obstinate this breed is.

I maintain that it's unnatural for a dog to look at its owner with disdain. Cats can get by with that crap, but I like to believe dogs hold themselves to a higher standard. I've faced Oscar down, determined to get my way, and been rejected, my commands met consistently with the canine equivalent of "You talking to me?"

He learned to unzip suitcases and rifle through unsuspecting guest's possessions, looking for snacks. Purses left unattended are opened and emptied in the blink of an eye. Compulsively larcenous, he was always on the lookout for something to chew up, steal, or swallow.

The women in our house defend the dog and absolve him of his indiscretions. They say he's cute and excuse his bad behavior. I accept reality. Oscar is in life for his own reward, and my safety or well being is of little consequence.

He's a "runner," prone to dawn escapes. His nose leads him forward with no thought of ever returning home. I've risked my life countless times, creeping through backyards in the early morning, searching for the dog, fearful I'd either be shot as a burglar or forced to return home and explain to my wife that he's missing. Meanwhile he's gone stealth, busy ripping open garbage bags down the block.

An accomplished hunter, chipmunks, squirrels, mice, and moles have all fallen prey to his quick and deadly jaws. Rabbits remain the prey of choice. They sneak into the garden through our iron-gate and feast on the frozen rosebushes in the moonlight. First thing every morning, both of our dogs, Oscar and Henry race out and chase rabbits around the yard until they leap through the gate and escape. Generations of rabbit kits have participated in this daily ritual, and the slow rabbits pay a tragic price.

In his prime I tied Oscar to a small plastic garden wagon. My thought was he could wander around with a measure of freedom but would not be able to disappear if he was dragging something. A rabbit unexpectedly appeared 100 feet down the driveway, and in an instant, the wiener dog was off, towing the wagon at warp speed. He caught the rabbit and dispatched it in seconds. I was impressed.

Two rabbits lifted their heads and fled when I let the dogs out today at 6 a.m. Henry, the younger of the two did several laps around the yard in hot pursuit while Oscar calmly observed from the sidelines. The thirteen-year-old dachshund wore a look of resignation instead of joining in.

It's not the first time I've felt compassion for the old dog, despite our challenging relationship. I shudder, watching him drag his junk through the snow on cold wintery days.

I've pursued all manner and shape of rabbit my entire life, but I've grown weary of the chase and resent spending my time and energy foolishly. There comes a moment in every beast's life when instinct or indignation takes a backseat to discretion and common sense. It's a peculiar comfort to accept our chasing days have ended.

7UP

When Kate was thirsty, she preferred water or tea. Never much for soft drinks, her sudden passion for 7UP took us by surprise.

She'd been admitted to a hospice three weeks earlier; a steady stream of friends and family did their best to make her comfortable. Visitors brought homemade soups, vegetable stews, and a wide variety of gifts. The small corkboard in her room was covered with cards and photos, a poster board annex had been constructed to handle the overflow. Vases of flowers lined the windowsill, letting a precious few sunbeams in to slow dance across her pink pillowcase. Someone was always bedside ready and eager to serve Kate in any way possible.

Coconut curry soup was a favorite, purchased at a local restaurant and spooned carefully into her mouth. She became animated as soon as the soup hit her tongue, "Oh my god!" she exclaimed, "The best soup ever. More! I could drink a gallon of this stuff." No soup in the history of the world had ever received the accolades and praise Kate lavished on the curry soup.

Kate was rarely demonstrative and never effusive. Her over-the-top reaction to soup was completely out of character. Nearing the end of her life, she seemed to be developing a flair for the dramatic.

Kate woke one day with a demand. "I want 7UP! Get me a cold can right away."

Her husband, Rick, a woman friend named Emma, and I had been sitting quietly as she slept. We looked at one another, uncertain we'd heard correctly.

"What, honey?" Rick asked. He looked puzzled.

"7UP." she repeated. "In a can and make it cold."

Emma leapt up off her chair. "I'll find you some, be right back." In a flash, she disappeared, seemingly relieved to have a mission.

Kate drifted off to sleep again, and Rick leaned over, asking me in a whisper, "Did she say 7UP? She never wants carbonated drinks." Rick is a little hard of hearing. I shrugged. "Maybe her stomach is upset?"

We waited for Emma to return. Before long she burst back

into the room, triumphantly announcing, "I've got it!" She took a seat next to the bed and popped open the can. The hiss awakened Kate, and she struggled, attempting to sit up.

"Isn't it just beautiful? I love how the can sparkles like a jewel." Kate was effusive. "Let me smell it." Emma held the can under Kate's nose, and she inhaled deeply before sinking back into her pillow and exhaling with a big smile on her face. "The most incredible smell ever. Someone should make 7UP perfume. Everyone would buy it. "Give me a sip," she said. "Help me sit up. I intend to enjoy this."

It took a few minutes to raise the bed and get her settled. She instructed us in no uncertain terms exactly how to set the stage. Pillows and blankets just so and the elevation of the bed adjusted precisely. She sat for a moment as if mentally checking for some forgotten detail before taking a deep breath and announcing, "I'm ready."

I admit I felt fear as Emma raised the can to Kate's lips. The sight and smell alone had sent her into rapture. God only knew what a sip would do.

Her eyes closed in bliss as she took her first sip. "Tell me about it."

"Beg your pardon?" Emma said.

"Tell me about it," Kate repeated. "I want you to tell me about 7UP while I drink."

Emma looked across the bed to Rick and me for guidance. She clearly didn't understand what on earth Kate was asking. Her confusion appeared close to panic. We weren't certain ourselves.

"Tell her about the soda, Emma," I coaxed, winking at her and pointing at the can. She began a frantic search of the can, speed-reading for details.

Kate cut her short. "More, another sip, that was spectacular. Tell me about it."

Emma raised the can, and Kate slowly sipped as Emma read, "It's clear and clean, ridiculously bubbly, and no caffeine."

I stifled a chuckle.

Kate opened one eye, peered at Emma, and said firmly, "Go on."

I felt for Emma, she meant well, but there is only so much you can say about 7UP. Or so we thought.

Kate overflowed with poetic descriptions of how it felt as it crossed her lips, caressing her tongue with millions of bubbles. She'd accept a sip, pause, swallow, and describe the graceful descent down her throat and the gentle yet building pressure in her tummy. Her sensual narrative went on, sip after sip, punctuated with delighted squeals and moans of pleasure.

I blushed.

Emma handed the can to Kate, wiped her hands on her jeans, and sat back, obviously shocked and suddenly embarrassed. Rick and

I avoided eye contact, pretending this intimate moment hadn't actually been brought to us by a beverage.

Kate fumbled with the can in her lap, and I asked if she needed help. "Yes," she said. "Pour some in my hands."

It was my turn to look for guidance. I wasn't about to pour a can of soda on a dying woman. Rick shrugged and nodded. Emma was having no part of this.

Kate held out both hands, palms up, and encouraged me. "Pour it."

I tipped the can slowly, but before any liquid came out, Kate stopped me. "That's enough." She raised her empty hands above her head and poured the imaginary "ridiculously bubbly" 7UP over her head.

She described every sensation in delicious detail, a self-satisfied grin on her face. I pictured her bathing naked in a clear mountain stream, shuddering in delight with each handful.

She raved about the restorative powers of the beverage, swearing she was ready to get up and go for a walk. "It's better than sex," she whispered, giggling to herself naughtily before falling fast asleep.

Emma excused herself and left the room. Rick sat next to Kate, holding her hand as she slept.

I saw Emma kneeling in the small chapel when I walked outside. I looked up at the autumn sky and wondered what on earth they might be putting in 7UP these days.

Never Finish Kate's Sentence

Kate died a week ago. She took excellent care of herself—ate the right foods, exercised, and stayed fit. It's not unreasonable to wonder how cancer could take her in scarcely nine months. I know the medical answer to my question, yet I still struggle to accept the random nature of mortality.

We'd known one another for over thirty years; however, our paths rarely crossed over the last fifteen. When we did meet, it was always easy to pick right up where we'd left off.

Kate was no stranger to death, having volunteered in hospice facilities over a period of decades and recently cared for her father with compassion as he walked through the final gate. I admit being curious how Kate would face her death, given how familiar she was with the process. My first visit to her hospice room satisfied my curiosity. A handwritten note was taped to her door.

Please limit visits to less than five minutes (except family). No more than four visitors at any given time, and don't finish my sentences.

Always clear, clean, and decisive, I could rely on Kate.

Hospice nurses say each death is unique and often reflects the way people lived their lives. Anxious, nervous people fret and fuss. Calm, melancholic people tend to leave peacefully, silently. Kate was a planner, always prepared and never shy about speaking up for what she wanted. I admired this quality, because I never felt a need to guess. I knew who she was and what she thought. She made it clear.

Cancer is a startling disease, shrinking the body in an astonishing manner and shocking the sensibilities, no matter how many times you brush against it. Her emaciated body no longer resembled the woman anchored in my memory. Only her broad smile and the bright spark in her eyes remained.

I visited repeatedly over the span of a couple of weeks. Kate drifted in and out, able to speak enough to let me know she appreciated my visits or sleeping deeply for hours, taking shallow breaths. At the end, lengthy conversation or "doing" is kept to a minimum. Exhaustion is a constant companion to the dying. Sitting bedside with the actively dying is an emotional challenge.

Kate lingered. Her strong heart kept a slow steady beat, ignoring the best guesses of medical staff. A nurse commented, "I've never seen anyone sit on the runway this long." She then turned to Kate, leaned in, and whispered, "Leap into the arms of Jesus, Kate."

Each visitor reassured Kate, letting her know she was loved and cared for and that she would be missed. "It's okay to let go," was whispered many times, yet she soldiered on, barely breathing.

The actively dying have their own agenda and loiter or leave with uncanny timing. Often a mystery to the living but so common it bears mention. Most have a list of things to finish before they finally feel complete. I've seen it repeatedly.

I wondered what she was completing.

We sat vigil with Kate her last three days, sharing stories or describing how we were connected to her. We became intimate with one another, gathered in a small circle around her bed. After each visit, I felt I had met new friends. I enjoyed the conversations, and they clearly revealed the qualities Kate valued in the people she invited into her life.

A week has passed since Kate died. I've thought of her often and puzzled over how long she lingered. Suddenly it struck me. Her "completion," what she finished those last days, became obvious. She'd silently introduced the people she loved to one another. She lingered so we could meet. I'm grateful for her love and having generously included me as a friend.

I never had to guess what Kate had on her mind. I simply had to listen patiently as she finished her sentence.

Christmas 1956

A magnificent twenty-foot tall Christmas tree stood in the center of the ballroom at the Sons of Norway Lodge, lights blazing. It was Sunday, December 23, 1956.

My five-year-old eyes reflected the lights while accordion and fiddle players coaxed old folk tunes from ivory keys and instruments made of leather and wood. Grandparents and generations of their children danced in a circle around the giant tree. The wooden dance floor groaned as they stamped their feet to the music. The air smelled of pine, wild-root hair tonic, and lilac perfume.

An army of aunts fueled the sweaty dancers with smoked ham, roast turkey, and baked delicacies, piling the plates high. They stuffed the children full of buttered lefse laced with sugar, frosting cookies shaped like stars, and then launched them, wild and laughing, into the crowd.

Uncles captained the bar, sloshing beer and whiskey into glasses or pouring shots of aquavit from bottles frozen in blocks of ice. The men teased the children into taking a "little sip" of the foul-smelling liquid, laughing loudly when we grimaced as the liquor hit our tongues.

Children ran through the crush of dancers or up the stairs to the balcony, where a flock of cousins had paused to catch their breath. We draped our arms over the railing and watched the glittery scene below.

Midway through the evening, Santa burst into the room and joined the dancers. Carrying an enormous bag of gifts over his shoulder, he shouted a hearty "Ho, Ho, Ho," startling the small children and amusing the grownups before excusing himself, explaining he had to return to his reindeer, waiting patiently on the roof with his sleigh.

Liquor, food, and exhaustion thinned the dancers, and many found chairs. I climbed into Grandpa's lap. His carpenter arms held me tight against a starched white shirt, and I listened to the deep rumble in his chest as he spoke Norwegian with the old-timers.

Their mysterious language fascinated me. They told stories of a sun that never set, mountains that cradled the sea, and trolls who lived in dark stone caverns. My earliest Christmas memories were formed in that large room, surrounded by old men sporting wide ties and their stoic, gray-haired wives.

Fellow immigrants. Each had once packed what little they owned, boarded crowded ships, and trusted a better life would be found in America. The lodge was proof of their success and testament to their hard work. Christmas was a time to celebrate the "American" life they had carved from poverty.

The evening always ended in the coatroom. We searched for our winter clothes amidst rows of rubber overshoes and a forest of wool overcoats. Bundled against the cold, we left the hot building through the oak double doors of the lodge and stepped onto a frosty sidewalk lined with snowbanks.

Station wagons and sedans bearing giant chrome bumpers idled patiently in the parking lot, warming to carry us home. My father led the way through rising columns of car exhaust tinted crimson by red taillights. He swung open the back door of our brown Chevrolet, so I could climb up and settle in the backseat. I pressed my bare hand on the window and melted a hole in the frost, watching the Christmas lights speed past as he drove us home through the city streets.

I'm no longer a wide-eyed five-year-old. Decades have passed since that Christmas party at the old Sons of Norway lodge.

The members built a modern new lodge in the '60 s. A bank now occupies the first floor. The building is a sound investment, but the top two floors have no balcony, and the low ceilings barely accommodate a ten-foot tree. Wooden dance floors are a relic of the past; carpeting covers the concrete floor. Our brown Chevrolet rusted long ago, and it's been years since I've heard Norwegian spoken fluently.

You might ask why I'm wandering through memories of Christmas past.

It all began several weeks ago, when a friend hosted an unusual pre-Christmas party in his home. He grew up in the house, his father died earlier this year and left him more than fifty years of memories and accumulated treasures in the rooms and crawl-spaces of the simple suburban home.

My friend attempted to empty memories from his boyhood home. Despite the fact the house was overflowing with treasure, an estate sale expert valued its contents at under $4000. Amazed that his father's possessions had so little worth, countless trips to the dump seemed the only reasonable option.

Roughly a dozen men gathered on a Tuesday evening during the last week in November, drawn by the host's provocative invitation:

Join us for some Christmas cheer. Arrive at 7:00 prepared to answer the following question: "What part of Christmas has died for you?"

You must excuse my cynical friend. He's had a hard couple of years and is approaching his mid-fifties and living in his father's house after suffering a lengthy divorce. His two teenage children live in a neighboring state, and he's facing the holidays alone in a house fully stocked with bittersweet memories.

His question does slip under the skin. Who among us hasn't wondered what happened to the holidays we remember from childhood? "Died" might be a bit strong. Certainly, Christmas never suffered a fatal blow, was hit by a bus or buried after a lingering illness. But clearly something happened to Christmas.

His question wormed its way through my mind, unearthing cynicism and curiosity. Had others suffered a similar loss? In our rush to maturity, had we misplaced Christmas? Despite our host's dark outlook, we arrived on a mild winter night, lured by the promise of a sealed bottle of fifty-year-old whiskey found tucked away in the basement bar.

Most of us are in our 50s and 60s, so the bottle of Kentucky whiskey was familiar. "Ancient Age" was a brand often stocked in the basement bars of our fathers and uncles. We settled in the near empty living room on a mismatched collection of old chairs gathered from throughout the house and ceremoniously opened the bottle.

A collection of innocently pornographic shot glasses discovered above the same bar held a splash of liquor for each of us. We had high hopes for the smoothness of the whiskey mellowing undisturbed in the basement for nearly as long as we'd been alive. One sip adjusted our expectations, and we got down to business.

The question that had drawn us to this gathering took some time to answer. It's easy to be cynical in November, when the marketing seduction is just ramping up. Maybe we hadn't heard enough Christmas carols yet or been subject to enough clever commercials to really get in the swing of things? Christmas grows on a man, by the third week of December, it's easy to lay down a credit card without flinching. However, late in November, Christmas still feels far out on the horizon.

Our opening attempts at an answer were full of resentment over the commercialization of Christmas and the ads for luxury cars played endlessly on television. None of us had ever known anyone who'd bought a luxury car as a gift, nor could we imagine doing so. We began firmly anchored in a Scrooge-like posture of judgment and skepticism. "Who killed Christmas?" It was all too easy to point at retailers, bankers and an economy driven by greedy and insatiable consumers.

Our initial approach was only the tip of the iceberg, and not really in keeping with the original question. "What part of Christmas has died for you?" was a very different question than "Who killed Christmas?"

A couple of the men looked uneasy. Not only uneasy with the question but also with the harshness they were using to speak about this most revered holiday. Naughty or nice came to mind. Privately pondering the erosion of Christmas was common but speaking our skepticism out loud in the company of others felt naughty.

Our host answered his original question. "This will be the first Christmas I will spend without my father. The part of Christmas he occupied was buried, along with his body."

Suddenly the erosion of Christmas became personal. Nothing at all to do with shameless marketing or commercialization, the uneasy feeling we shared regarding his question hinted at the losses we had suffered. We began to understand why this thorny question was so compelling.

"What part of Christmas has died for you?"

One of the men picked up the thread. After taking a sip of his whiskey and shifting his Betty Boop shot glass from one hand to the other, he said, "I divorced a year ago. I live in a small apartment downtown, and I doubt I'll even get to see my kids during the holidays. Part of Christmas died when I divorced. I expected to be surrounded by my family every holiday through my life, but I've had to let the dream go. The part that died for me was family."

Silence.

His words landed hard. Any righteous indignation fled the room, and we were left holding one of the sharpest blades ever to cut a man's heart: divorce. Separated from the family he had shaped his future around, he approached Christmas anticipating little but a promise of loneliness and regret.

Another man spoke of large family holidays held in the home he'd recently sold. He and his wife and children had gathered every Christmas morning for twenty years to open gifts in their living room. Now their children were grown, with homes and families of their own. They could no longer justify staying in the large rambling home, where they'd raised a family.

"I traded my home for a large check and a small condo," he said.

"Selling my house forced me to see my children had grown up and moved on. I'll still celebrate with them, but they're adults. The kids who sang carols with me around the piano are gone. My living room belongs to another family. Even my piano grew legs and found a new place. Part of Christmas died when I sold my house."

One by one, they answered the question as best they could. As the evening progressed, stories of love, loss, and time on the march swirled around the room. Not all the stories were sad. Beautiful memories of Christmas past mixed with the whiskey disappearing from the bottle of Ancient Age.

We grew melancholic and tender, speaking of grandchildren soon to arrive from out of town for a week of grandpa time. We shared fond memories of the fathers who went to extraordinary lengths to make sure the stage was set just so before opening the doors of the family room and ushering their children into a wonderland of decorations and wrapped presents on Christmas morning. Precious gifts were mentioned, toys long ago worn out and discarded, symbols of how much their parents had sacrificed to make them happy.

We ended the evening full of gratitude for the few hours that had sparked so much dormant emotion. In a peculiar way, this thorny question had actually softened our hearts.

"What part of Christmas has died for you?"

I replayed the stories in my mind on the way home. A wide range of beautiful Christmas memories and heartbreaking disappointments combined to conjure a larger picture of Christmas than I imagined possible. Men held a string in each hand. One led into the past and what we remembered, and the other stretched into the future toward our hopes and expectations.

I've buried most of my family over the years. My children are grown, and I've had to reluctantly say goodbye to the kids they once were. Bits of Christmas were released with each passage.

I lingered outside when I arrived home, feeling a deep longing for my grandpa. I miss my family. Mother and father, my grandmas and grandpas, the many uncles and aunts who'd worked so hard, so love could illuminate the dark. Glitter, shiny wrapping paper, and extravagant gifts only reflect the light. Love is what I long for, not a pale reflection, recreation, or fantasy.

I looked up at the dome of stars in the dark winter sky and realized all the trappings of Christmas meant little to me. Gifts, food, and parties were little but a stage set. Christmas remained the most human of rituals, generosity and love end up as the enduring intention.

Christmas has a life cycle mirroring our own. Childlike wonder evoked by Santa or the birth of the Christ child in a manger matures through the years into a ship loaded with loving acts adrift in a sea of memories.

I wondered if my grandfathers reached a certain age, only to discover their hearts full to the brim with memories and emotion? If the Norwegian words I couldn't understand when I'd snuggled safe in Grandpa's lap so many years ago were similar to the words my friends had spoken tonight? Words of love, loss, and Christmas past, teased to the surface during the time of year when light is in the shortest supply.

Endings Demand Emotion

Diana's one of the lucky ones, able to feel deeply without inhibition or excuse. She was in her early thirties when she re-connected with her grandmother. The previous three decades had been punctuated by long periods of estrangement. They'd grown apart and scarcely knew one another. Diana's compassion had brought them together.

The old woman was living in a nursing home, terminally ill and approaching ninety. She'd been an angry woman, self-centered and painfully manipulative. Her behavior permanently damaged relationships with friends and family, and she was confronting the end of life, isolated and alone.

Diana was motivated to seek her out, driven by a compelling desire for family. Often feeling like an outcast, she couldn't abide the thought of her grandmother facing death alone. Her visits were a compassionate offering to an old woman but also served her desire to discover where she came from and an even deeper longing to find where she belonged.

As it often does, illness and age had softened her. Grandmother made peace with her terminal diagnosis and refused treatment that could only postpone the inevitable. As cancer gripped her, it seemed to wrestle her heart open, and she turned the page on her previous behavior.

Diana recognized this shift and began making frequent visits to her grandmother's bedside, often bringing some small treat requested by the old woman. Neither saw much benefit in re-visiting old wounds. They sought peace in the present moment, united by the unbreakable bond of lineage. The two women built a bridge spanning a hurtful past, offering simple kindness to one another and moving beyond the neglect scarring previous years.

They often wept together, fully accepting time was limited and this rekindled love would soon end. When tears made words difficult, the old woman would take Diana's face in her hands, wipe the tears from her cheeks, and smooth her dark hair. She would reassure the young woman in a soothing voice. "It's all right, honey. I'm sorry. I love you."

As her Grandmothers health declined, Diana's visits had less to do with words and more to do with attending to her care. She spent hours fussing over her grandmother's hair and nails or gently rubbing sweet-smelling lotion into her skin. Physical kindness seemed the most meaningful and satisfying expression of love.

One morning the phone call came from the care facility. Grandma was close to the end. The small family gathered around her bed as a hospice nurse explained, "Her lungs are barely functioning, and her breathing is extremely shallow. With no intervention, as per her wishes, she will die in a matter of hours."

Long years and hard feelings had worn this family thin. They seldom spent time together, and watching life slowly drain from the matriarch did little to put them at ease. They made small talk, reminiscing and re-telling stories gone stale from being told one too many times, and they avoided the prickly memories.

Any change in the old woman's breathing, and all eyes would focus on the bed expectantly. Is this it? A ragged inhale would answer the question.

Late in the afternoon, the moment arrived. A long exhale followed by no inhale. Minutes passed with no breath, and silence blanketed the room. Someone pressed the call button, and they stood staring, avoiding one another's eyes, uncertain what to say as they waited for a professional to confirm what they already knew.

The nurse entered the room, felt for the old woman's pulse, turned to face those gathered, and said, "I'm so sorry, she's gone."

These words always hang with astounding gravity in a room.

As much as we may accept the reality, or even witness the end, this final proclamation makes the ending incredibly real. The nurse searched the silent faces. "Take as much time as you need. Let me know if you have any questions, and stop by the nurse's station to let us know when you leave." One of the sons finally spoke up. "What happens now?" His voice cracked like that of a frightened, confused child.

The nurse said, "After you leave, a doctor will sign the death certificate, and the body will be moved to the morgue. Once you've made arrangements, the mortician will collect the body and prepare for the funeral. Be sure and take her personal effects with you."

The nurse left, and the door closed slowly behind her.

Diana squeezed between her father and uncle to the edge of the bed. She pulled the blanket back, revealing the old woman's lifeless body wrapped in a thin cotton robe. Without hesitation she slid her arm gently under her grandmother's shoulders, crawled into the bed, and lay next to her, holding her close. She tenderly smoothed her grandmother's hair as she wept.

The impact of this most intimate action on those gathered was profound. Guided by emotions as old as mankind, and ignoring any inhibition, Diana offered a final embrace and unwittingly led her family beyond a shared history of resentment.

Hands previously frozen in place reached out to touch their mother one last time. Tears flowed freely as they felt the absence of life in a body that had once provided the gift of life. The family found comfort in the liberation that accompanies forgiveness.

A new mythology took root in Diana's family the day Grandma died. The old familiar story of neglect and resentment began to erode, and a greater myth of compassion and forgiveness was born. To this day, those present look back on Diana's final embrace as a crossroad, grateful for her uninhibited grief.

Humans are intended to touch and be touched. This last embrace may be the most cathartic, wordlessly reminding us what we may have neglected, forgotten, or forgiven.

The Mortician

I eased into an empty parking space between a hearse and a long limousine. My truck matched the black color scheme perfectly. I was struck by how silent this place was the moment I stepped onto the asphalt.

Mortuaries intentionally tailor the surrounding landscape to evoke a sense of serene calm, dampening the sound of neighborhood traffic with massive beds of day lilies, evergreens, and thoughtfully placed maples.

The parking lot was empty. Eight thirty in the morning was far too early for a funeral, I guessed. A massive lot was a required feature. Parking for mourners but also space to accommodate the armada of cars that must be assembled in one long line for the drive to the gravesite. Traffic management was a critical part of funerals.

I'd watched a motorcycle cop herd cars into formation when I stopped to make my appointment a few days ago. He'd reminded me of a no-nonsense sheepdog, using his motorcycle to nudge rather dense motorists into single file for the trek to the cemetery. He played two roles: traffic cop and motorized shepherd, racing ahead of the procession to the next set of stoplights, blocking the impatient cross traffic and backtracking to gather up strays.

I was meeting with the mortician as part of a series of interviews I was doing with people engaged in the business of death. Well, "business" might be a little unfair. I was researching the emotional pressures felt by people who brushed against death daily in their workday world. I'd interviewed clergy, doctors, nurses, and hospice workers.

The mortuary exuded a feeling of dignity. Ten-foot high colonial double doors defined the entrance, which was bracketed by massive limestone columns. The scale of the architecture was larger than life. As I pulled the brass door handle, the weight of the door made me feel like a small child, struggling in a world built for much larger people.

The two-story foyer did little to put me at ease. A spectacular floor-to-ceiling wall of rough limestone anchored the far end of the room, and a long narrow reflecting pool collected the perpetual fall of water flowing down the stone wall. I felt as though I was standing in a large wet cave. The building was silent, except for the sound of the water trickling across stones.

Two chapels were available, one to the right and one to the left. Wooden easels holding a collage of photographs stood sentry outside the closed doors. They displayed poignant moments of life culled from old albums and scrapbooks, neatly organized chronologically late at night by a loved one armed with a jar of paste. The photos hinted at who was lying behind the closed chapel doors, the lives they lived, and the people they cared about.

An older woman emerged from one of the offices lining a long hallway. She walked briskly toward me, dressed in a conservative black business suit. Her most remarkable feature was her head of perfectly sculpted iron-gray hair. I find older women's hairstyles remarkable feats of engineering, often shaped in the most extraordinarily un- hair-like manner and then frozen mysteriously in place.

"Can I help you?" Her manner was clipped, efficient.

"I have an appointment with Richard McGreevy." "Your name?" she asked.

"Snake Bloomstrand." The woman offered one arched eyebrow and a piercing look to test whether I was serious. "Please follow me." Turning abruptly, she walked back to her office, with me trailing her.

"I'll let Mr. McGreevy know you are here, Mr. Bloomstrand."

She spoke over her shoulder, putting emphasis on "mister."

After whispering a few words into the phone, she turned back to me. "I'll show you to a consulting room. He is just finishing up and will meet with you shortly."

In the spirit of small talk, I offered, "I've been interviewing people who work around death. I've yet to talk to a mortician."

She paused, once again locking eyes with me, and corrected in a stern voice. "We prefer mortuary technician."

My attempt to use conversation to crack her professional shield a disaster, I followed obediently and silently down the long hallway.

She ushered me into a room furnished with half a dozen upholstered chairs and a large mahogany desk. "Please take a seat." She closed the door and left me alone in the room.

Lamps lit the room with a subdued light and small gold-framed notices were strategically placed on the mahogany side tables to inform clients, *Credit terms are available* and *Payment must be made in full before day of service.* Thick volumes with laminated pages were stacked on the table, detailing an assortment of coffins and flower arrangements.

A tall man in a well-tailored black suit entered the room and introduced himself. "I'm Richard McGreevy. Sorry to keep you waiting. I had to sign for some deliveries, and it took longer than I anticipated. I understand you need some information. How can I help?"

He settled at his desk as I described my research with various professionals. I had a list of questions prepared, and he agreed to do his best to answer them.

"What attracted you to this profession?" I asked.

Mr. McGreevy said, "I've been in the business for over twenty-five years and began my career at this very mortuary, right out of college. I grew up in a small Wisconsin town, and my uncle was the local mortician. I worked part-time for him before going off to the university.

"The funeral business has changed over the years. I went to school intending to come home and work with my uncle, but he sold the business before I graduated.

"When I started, mortuaries were mom and pop operations. We built relationships with the families we served and really felt like a part of the community. Although many of us held on to our business names, most mortuaries are now owned by corporate entities. Same for the casket suppliers and the chemical companies that supply the embalming fluids we depend on. Like so many businesses, profitability has become far more complicated as the industry has grown."

"What other changes have you seen?" I asked.

"Well, we offer a wide range of services we didn't years ago. We've had to become more flexible and creative," he replied. "Our clients now come from a wider range of ethnic backgrounds. Each culture has different beliefs and traditions. We try to accommodate the families as best we can. Christian or Jewish services used to be the norm. Now we serve that clientele, along with Muslims from the Middle East or Buddhists from Asia. We have associates within these communities to assure relevant procedures and rituals are observed.

"I'm a Catholic and see my work as that of a facilitator, guiding people through a series of unfamiliar and difficult decisions. The goal is to shape a meaningful service that will honor the departed. I love my work." He added, "I can't imagine doing anything else. I feel a real sense of satisfaction in providing a service that's in keeping with my spiritual beliefs. Adapting services to fit beliefs other than my own has been a challenge and at the same time expanded my spirituality.

"Muslims have very specific rituals when preparing a body for burial. Special care is taken to clean and wrap the body. The process must be accomplished with intention. It's quite beautiful." He paused.

I gave him a moment, then asked why he'd stopped.

"One change does bother me. Increasingly we see clients who are not interested in a funeral. Cremation is so popular these days. Families simply call us to collect the body, usually from a hospital or extended care facility, and ask us to let them know when the ashes are ready to pick up. No funeral. I believe family and friends miss out on a sense of closure when the funeral is skipped. I think a proper tribute to the individual's life and a place to gather is important." As an afterthought, just in case I'd misunderstood, he added, "Sure, it is my business, but closure, and some manner of honoring the loved one only seems the right thing to do. I can't imagine a death with no service. I remember a closet in the basement of my uncle's mortuary, where we stored boxes of unclaimed ashes. We called it the 'sad closet.'

"I'm sure some families spread ashes according to the wishes of the departed. I even know of a company that loads shotgun shells or fireworks with ashes. At least time and intention are paid to the end of a life, even if that ending only amounts to an explosion. But I wonder how many ashes sit for years on a shelf, gathering dust after they are picked up?"

"What would you say is the most challenging aspect of your job?" I asked. I could see he was an earnest man, considering each of my questions thoughtfully before replying.

"Often the families are especially upset."

"What do you mean?" "Sometimes they are estranged or haven't been in the same room together in years. When a relative dies, they feel an obligation to participate in the decisions. They come into my office and make the arrangements with some measure of grief or loss, but they also bring any resentment or un-resolved issues along with them. I need to be a counselor, psychologist, and sometimes even a referee. I've had near fist fights break out over the color of a casket." He leaned toward me, confiding, "You realize of course, the argument wasn't about the color scheme. It probably began years before and festered until that moment."

"What advice would you give families?" "To try and resolve any differences before a funeral. It's far too late by that time and distracts everyone from the business at hand. Putting a loved one to rest is no time to squabble over ancient history or hurt feelings.

"Occasionally the conflict is centered on a will or inheritance, and survivors feel they have been treated unfairly. It must be like a slap in the face to be left out of a will. I often wonder where this mean-spirited behavior comes from. Some of the departed use their will as a weapon to punish from beyond the grave, like a dark shadowy way to get the last word.

"I have a theory that death can bring out the worst in people. Not always, but often enough. It makes my job difficult, but that's the least of it. The survivors remain miserable and resentful for a lifetime. If only families would speak honestly with one another, so much heartache could be avoided."

I liked Mr. McGreevy. He seemed to be a genuinely compassionate man, intelligent and considerate. We had established some rapport, and I now felt prepared to ask the questions that were really on my mind.

"How do you cope with facing grieving families day in day out? Does the emotional part of this business weigh on you?"

"Hard questions to answer. I suppose you do get used to it after a time. I struggled with getting too close to the families early in my career. I felt more like a relative, and if anything went wrong, I took it personally. These days, I have better boundaries, and I'm able to leave work at work when the day is over. He went silent again, staring out the window and avoiding eye contact.

"Did you want to say something else?" I asked. Silence. I had decided to push gently when I noticed tears welling in his eyes. "I can see something is troubling you," I prodded. "I am writing about the emotional impact on professionals who handle the details of death. Anything you can offer is of great value to me."

"It's going to sound ironic." "Emotions often are ironic." He took a Kleenex from a decorative box next to his chair and wiped his eyes, then tossed it into one of the three trashcans in the room. He acted as if wanted to share a secret and said in a whisper, "My mother is dying. I don't expect her to live another three months. I have been unable to speak honestly with her or my family about the situation. I'm afraid I'll jinx her." The mortician began to weep.

I'm afraid I'll jinx her?

My interviews had proven people were curious and willing when I introduced the topic of death. Most had opinions and were grateful for the conversation, but his words struck me like a lightning bolt. In a world where emotion carried great consequences, we tended to avoid the whole subject. Were we convinced emotion would overwhelm us, making it impossible to speak at all, or would death show up instantly if we uttered its name?

He apologized. "I realize how foolish that must sound, I know better. I'm sorry."

"Not at all," I replied. "The range of emotion I've encountered is wide and varied. Professionalism doesn't eliminate emotion, whether we are a doctor, nurse, or member of the clergy. In fact, the roles we play, or the authority we wield, tends to drive emotion further underground. Some of the people I've interviewed were angry or wracked with guilt. We don't speak of the emotions surrounding death often enough to become agile. We rarely talk about emotion, period. Yet we all live in our private soup of feelings. I really appreciate your honesty." Mr. McGreevy seemed reassured and strained to regain his composure. "I know I need to speak with Mother and my family, and I will. I just keep waiting for the right time."

"I understand." The shameless facilitator in me wanted to dig into his avoidance, but I figured he'd probably had enough of me, and my list of questions. I decided to end the interview. Besides, I was more than satisfied with bringing a mortician to tears.

I thanked him for being open with me. I assured him he'd been helpful, and wished him well with his difficult conversation.

He walked me to the door, still red-eyed and a little wobbly. He stopped to ask the receptionist if his next appointment had arrived, and she must have spotted his puffy eyes, because she shot me the stink eye. We shook hands, and he said, "I will speak to my family."

His words stayed with me. I stood outside, soaking in the morning sun next to an enormous bed of day lilies, reviewing our conversation in my mind.

"I'm afraid I'll jinx her."

I've felt that way, frightened that if I speak of what I fear, I'll embolden it in some unconscious manner.

His advice to families—"Speak what needs to be spoken before a death occurs"—is good advice. It is ironic that a man capable of guiding so many families through this passage would find it so difficult to find his own way. Once death visits, it is too late for words.

Last week, when I visited a large local hospital, the receptionist asked me why I was interviewing doctors. I explained, and her reaction was straightforward. She waved a hand in the direction of the busy, crowded lobby and declared, "Death? It certainly is the elephant in the room, isn't it?"

As I walked to my truck, I noticed Mr. McGreevy watching me through a window. I nodded in his direction, but he quickly dropped the curtain and disappeared.

The Fish Bat

A mutual friend called to inform me about Jon Fish and his sudden illness.

Jon had been hospitalized with pneumonia, and soon after, the doctors discovered cancer spreading rapidly through his major organs, spine, and brain. Doctors gave him a week to live. Jon was fifty-six years old.

I called his wife, Rita, and she filled me in on his condition. I asked how she was doing.

Jon's rapid decline had left her largely speechless. "I know I'm in shock. It's going to take time before I know how I feel."

Rita handed the phone to Jon, and we shared a brief uncomfortable moment. How did one begin what may be a final conversation? Several years had passed since we'd last spoken, but despite the circumstances, we reconnected quickly. We'd loved one another through the years, regardless of the distance.

I remembered a gift he had given me some twenty years ago —a scarred wooden baseball bat.

It had his name—Fish—painted in big messy letters on the business end of the bat. He'd owned it for years, and when he gave it to me, he explained it was a magic bat. A no-strike-out bat. We shared one of those rare loving moments that happen when men give something they hold precious to a friend. At the time, I had a house full of eight-year-old boys who were crazy for baseball. I passed the bat and the myth on to them. The "Fish bat" became legendary. The boys checked to make sure it was in the equipment bag before each game. I'd watch them carry the bat to the plate and face down any pitcher with confidence.

That summer they believed they couldn't strike out if their hands were wrapped around that bat. Each time I heard the crack and watched the ball take flight, I would think of Jon, his generous gift kept us wordlessly connected. The Fish bat was magical.

I reminded Jon of it, explaining how the boys had turned it into a sacred object.

"No shit!" A man rarely gets a peek at his legacy.

I'd recently become a grandfather and joked with Jon, "You're going to have to call me by my new name."

"You changed your name from Snake?"

"Well, sort of. Now you can call me Grampy Snake."

Jon laughed. "What did they name the baby?"

"Oscar," I announced. "Oscar Bloomstrand. Sounds like someone you'd meet ice fishing, doesn't it?"

I heard Jon call to his wife, "Rita, tell Snake our new grandson's name."

I heard her response in the background. "Oscar."

We ended our conversation with a moment of blessed synchronicity.

Affection

Wisdom can sneak in the back door, appearing in hindsight and confirming the time a father spends with his children become the investment of a lifetime.

I read storybooks to my two-year-old grandson. He climbs on my lap, snuggles into my chest, and we read books full of sing-song poetry and whimsical drawings.

"I do not like green eggs and ham. I do not like them, Sam-I am!" –Suess

The storybooks are a means to an end, an investment. I didn't fully realize, when my young children crawled on my lap for a story thirty years ago, this investment would pay such magnificent dividends. The payoff is affection.

My son arrived recently to collect my grandson. I asked about his day, and he spoke of challenging work, tight schedules, and a shortage of time. While his father sat on the floor next to my chair, the toddler pushed brightly colored cars across the carpet.

We were speaking about the small bits and pieces of life that add up to exhaustion when my son unexpectedly laid his head on my knee. I stroked his head as I had done for so many years. My grandson watched us closely, and curious about this obvious affection between his father and grandfather, he abandoned his cars, came close, and laid his head on my other knee.

Affection: *a rare state of mind or body associated with feeling love.*

Man or woman, young and old, the desire for affection never ends. An affectionate father responds to this hunger because he's felt the hunger himself. A wise father comes to realize moments of affection remain relevant for a lifetime.

Affection can sneak in the back door and make a father's heart swell.

The Medical Examiner

One beautiful summer afternoon, Jerry and I decided to hop on an old rusty freight train. Our leather sandals kicked up the gravel along the tracks as we ran on twelve-year- old legs, determined to catch the steel ladder welded to the boxcar.

We each grabbed a rung and pulled up with all our might. Feet firmly planted on the bottom rung, and trusting the strength in our thin, young arms to keep us safe, we leaned back. The wind blew the hair from our sunburnt faces, and we laughed. I felt like a bird, flying along the tracks.

We were headed for the beach and nearly to the strip of cattails and marsh grass bordering the shoreline of the lake. We got ready to jump. As Jerry leapt for the long grass, his sandal caught on the bottom rung.

He dangled by one foot for a split-second, wide-eyed, knowing, then the heavy steel wheels swallowed him. A medical examiner walked those tracks fifty years ago, collecting the bits and pieces of my friend, scattered between the steel rails. Jerry's accident was my first encounter with death and would not be the last. The M E was dressed in a black suit, carrying a black bag and doing his job, trained and paid to determine cause of death.

Eight boys stood alongside the tracks, watching in horror. We all made a silent promise to never again steal a ride on a train. Somehow Jerry's sandals ended up on the cement base of the crossing signal. I suppose someone found them along the tracks and placed them where the owner might be able to reclaim them. Jerry's sandals sat there for months. None of us would touch them.

An ME pulled into my driveway this past Sunday. Not the tall, thin man I remember from my childhood. This one hadn't arrived to collect my boyhood friend. This one carried a colorful purse instead of a large black bag.

My dogs took their job seriously and barked incessantly when anyone arrived. A pretty blonde woman appeared at the gate.

"You must be Ellie?" I said, shooing the dogs out of the way. "Good to meet you. Welcome." I opened the gate. "Please ignore the dogs. They may sound ferocious, but in ten minutes they'll be wanting to sit in your lap."

"You must be Snake." She laughed. "No worry about the dogs. I have two little bulldogs. I'm used to the ruckus."

The medical examiner had arrived.

"Your garden is amazing," she said, scanning the July flowers blanketing the yard. "I see why you asked me to meet you at your house. This is spectacular."

I introduced Ellie to the people gathered on the patio. My wife, Alexis, and one of her daughters, Alicia, sat at a small granite table. Two of my friends, Edmond and Randall, slid back and forth on the glider. A passionate discussion was underway, and Ellie seemed amused.

Alicia had been educating us in the fine art of women's shoes before Ellie arrived. I'd heard it before, but Edmond and Randall were getting a crash course. They wore a look of shock as Alicia patiently explained the very expensive and complicated art of hunting down the perfect pair of heels.

The shoes she described, in suggestive detail, came with exotic names rivaling the pricey sports cars of the world: Maserati, Ferrari, and Bentley. The shoes were little sculptures made of bits of exotic leather and wood. They were meant to hold, display, or on occasion, torture a foot. Edmond and Randall hadn't walked across fire like I had. I'd been on the hunt with these women. The two men had no idea how serious shoe collecting could be.

Edmond said, "This shoe thing is scary enough, but are you

going to talk about death again? If you are, I'm leaving. Last time the conversation was steered in that direction, you completely ruined my cheesy potato dinner." Edmond's forty-eight-year-old body was beginning to falter. He blamed his love of food. Actually, he was one of many men, growing older and beginning to see his body as less than reliable, and fearing the certainty of mortality.

"Yes, we are going to speak about death. Ellie came to offer her viewpoint. Ellie is a medical examiner."

I'd been introduced me to her via e-mail. She and her husband were part of a larger circle of friends. My daughter Anna had joked, "We call Ellie Dr. Death."

Two weeks ago, Ellie and I had undertaken the e-mail ritual of setting a time and place to meet, settling on Sunday afternoon in my garden. Ellie was in her mid-thirties, roughly my daughter's age. She was dressed in jeans, sandals, and a white T-shirt. She was open, friendly, and took the dogs and all the shoe chatter in stride, as well as the inevitable references to *CSI*.

Alexis asked if her job was like the TV show.

Ellie laughed and explained that her job as a medical examiner didn't resemble a television drama and no, she had never met Mark Harmon. Ellie had a good sense of humor and fit in easily.

"How did you become an ME?" Randall asked.

"I went through medical school to become a doctor. I developed an interest in forensics and did a three-year residency in

New York, working primarily in the Bronx and Queens. Working in New York was an experience. Medical examiners in large cities see a lot of human drama."

"Well, I can see where this conversation is headed." Edmond said. "I better leave before you spoil my dinner again." He said his goodbyes, then Ellie, Randall, and I wandered through the garden to my studio.

I admit stereotypes get in my way at my age. I'd expected her to resemble a tall serious man in a black suit. The thought of someone so young being a doctor confused my sixty-year-old brain, and I struggled to replace my outdated image of a medical examiner with the lovely, professional woman who had agreed to speak with us.

We settled into comfortable chairs in my studio, and I explained my purpose for inviting her to this conversation. "Tell me about your specific duties." I said.

"As a medical examiner, my responsibility is to determine the cause of death. I may go to the location and investigate, will certainly perform an autopsy, and file an official report. I call the family, inform them of my determination, and answer any questions they may have."

"Are they difficult calls to make?"

"Some are. Best case, I'm able to answer their questions. Worst case, they disagree with my findings."

"What do you mean?" Randall asked.

"The death of a family member can bring out the worst in people. Sometimes they feel guilty and want to shift any feeling of responsibility for the death onto someone else—a doctor or nurse, or they might want to blame a nursing home or hospital for not providing adequate care. Sad to say, some try to manipulate the circumstances of a death for insurance reasons. Natural death doesn't always pay off in the same way as an accident.

"Most of the calls I make are routine. The survivors accept what I've discovered and are grateful for my explanation." Ellie was straightforward and candid.

"Are you always able to identify cause of death? Are there cases where you are uncertain?" I asked.

"Cause of death is a clinical determination." She explained, "I make observations and perform an autopsy. This tells me the facts, like heart failure or blood loss. Respiratory failure is another common cause of death. You'd be amazed how many people young and old die of suffocation. People with severe asthma or even pneumonia can smother in their pillows or blankets, and this is often where uncertainty appears.

"The circumstances of a death can be open to interpretation. The death of a baby or a young child is the hardest for people to accept. Parents often suffer crushing guilt and endless second-guessing. But it's not only the aged that die of natural causes." Ellie added sarcastically, "In our culture there is no such thing as natural death."

I understood what she was saying. Several people I'd interviewed had alluded to how "managed" death is in Western culture. Doctors and nurses are seen as having failed if a patient dies. Medicine is falsely believed to cure all diseases, and when it doesn't, the practitioner is often blamed for the shortcomings of the treatment they recommended. Fact is, people die.

Ellie's job afforded an unusual vantage point. She witnessed families at their most vulnerable and with a frequency the rest of us could only imagine.

"I appreciate your willingness to speak about your job." I said, "The title 'medical examiner' has always been police-like in my mind. I guess I've been influenced by television, but I'm also interested in the emotional impact on you now that I better understand your responsibilities."

Ellie paused before replying. "I've been thinking about your questions since you suggested we meet. I don't remember ever being asked how I feel about my job. I hardly know where to begin. Dealing with families does stir up a lot of feelings, and some of my coworkers grow hard. I guess a wall between work and home is a good thing. I've just never been able to brick it up completely."

Ellie looked Randall and me over, checking to see if we were really safe to talk with. She must have decided we were safe enough, because as soon as she started speaking, she teared up. Her words were heartfelt, revealing her emotional agility and range.

"I should explain my tears. I had the worst year of my life a while back. Several people I cared about died. It was horrible, six deaths in one year. They included a suicide, an accident, and the murder of my aunt. I was living in New York City, far from friends and family, and surrounded by death at work every day. It seemed to follow me home as well.

"I'd adjusted easily when I started. Death was part of my job, and I felt prepared for the emotional part of it. My coworkers were helpful, offering valuable coaching to the "new girl," but when people I loved began to die, it became personal. I was awake most nights, worrying or crying.

"The friends I'd made were mostly in their late twenties and didn't understand what I was on about. I couldn't bear to hang out at the bars, talking about superficial topics, and no one really wanted to hear what was going on in my life, because it was so incredibly sad and depressing.

"When people did ask how I was, and I'd begin to tell them, their eyes showed the truth. They wanted to support me, but the degree of sadness I felt frightened them. They didn't know what to say and usually tried to cheer me up. I wasn't in the mood to be cheery. I felt gloomy, heavy, and full of grief. I was isolated and spent much of my free time alone. I felt so lonely I'd call home and talk to my dad every night.

"Then my grandma became ill, and I hit bottom." Tears flowed down her cheeks.

I was surprised someone so tender hearted could do her job so well.

She wiped tears away and continued. "My understanding of death moved far beyond anything I'd learned in medical school when grandma died. Medical school gave me the knowledge and credentials to manage the mechanics of life and death. Grandma's death forced me to face the limitations of my education. I couldn't 'fix' her, and I felt completely powerless.

"I went home for a couple of weeks, to be with her near the end. I sat by her bedside, watching her decline. I made sure she ate and stayed hydrated, but then she refused food and wouldn't drink. I knew medically what was happening, but I was reluctant to let go. I'd been trained to keep people alive.

"A hospice nurse took me aside after watching me force a glass of water into Grandma. She patiently explained that as people die, their bodies begin to shut down, and when they refuse sustenance, its simply one of many signs they are near death. It makes everyone miserable if we ignore the signs that signal the end of treatment and the start of letting-go.

"I knew this. I'd been taught it, but never fully understood the emotional limitations until faced with the death of someone I loved. If my professors had taught how to let go, the lesson never sank in. The line between a patient and a loved one is where the difficult lessons are learned.

"Grandma's death was cathartic. I faced the place where medicine confronts emotion and must surrender to the limitations of science. The hospice nurse taught me a lesson every doctor should learn. The 'God complex' doctors are often accused of and nurses complain bitterly about gets in the way of accepting that we all die. Denying death doesn't serve anyone."

She'd shared a profound understanding of the dilemma all healthcare workers face. The limitations of medicine make acceptance of death unavoidable.

"I really appreciate being able to talk about this." Ellie wiped her eyes. "When I'm with people my own age, conversation tends toward daycare providers, home decorating, and the latest restaurants. The serious nature of death can be a real conversation killer." Ellie smiled at the irony. "My friends know what I do for a living. They make all the predictable jokes, and I'm not always so serious. In fact, when I finished medical school, my friends threw a big graduation party for me. They made me a set of black scrubs decorated with silver studs, skulls and crossbones, and embroidered Dr. Death in big letters on the back. I appreciated the time and attention they put into the costume, but the serious side of what I do is always just under the surface.

"Raising babies or remodeling a home belongs to a different

phase of life, and end of life discussions don't mix well with the concerns of starting a family."

"What about the people you work with? Certainly, you speak with them." I said.

"Not often," she replied. "We talk about our cases but not about how we feel. The wall I spoke of earlier gets in the way. Over time it divides our professional selves from who we are as people. For some this wall becomes impenetrable. They completely brick off their private lives and limit any interaction to their professional duties.

"Others struggle with these boundaries, as if the bricks keep crumbling, leaving them exposed and vulnerable. They tend to be the ones who move on to another specialty. The stress is simply too much for them. I fall somewhere in between and rarely get a chance to speak like I have today."

"I really appreciate how honest and open you've been, Ellie," Randall offered,

"I wonder how many professions offer this rare opportunity to look at life and death from such an unusual perspective. I'm struck by the idea of a wall separating work from emotion. Certainly, doctors and nurses create that wall. Every profession requires boundaries but witnessing the end of a life requires extreme emotional boundaries I never considered.

" Your profession puts you face to face with mortality every day. I can only imagine the emotions that surface. You really don't have the luxury of cultural denial. The hard truth shows up in your workplace every day."

"I don't want to sound like it's a burden," Ellie replied. "The perspective I've gained is realistic. I'm not fatalistic. I simply accept the entire life cycle. Birth, life, and death. Like it or not, it's a complete package."

We were silent for a moment. Ellie's comment hit bone. A complete package. This young ME had squeezed a lot of wisdom from her career so far. It was hot in my studio, and although the fan was pushing the humid air around the room, Ellie's honesty added another flavor of heat.

I'm not sure what I expected when I extended the invitation, but so far Ellie had me thinking beyond anything I had imagined.

"Can I answer the other question you asked me?" Ellie asked.

"Which one?" I responded.

"You asked me what insight I've gained as a result of what I do. I've spent a lot of time thinking about that. I've learned about people and their families, coworkers, and how they can struggle. I've learned to be a competent doctor and am better able to deal with the limitations of my training, but one glaring insight did surface." Ellie went quiet and looked out over the garden.

"Please go on," I said.

"It's going to sound grisly."

"Don't worry about that," I said. "I'm well past any uneasiness. Everyone I've interviewed has offered a piece of the puzzle, and I'm grateful."

Ellie looked us over once again. "One aspect of my job has really influenced how I see people. Rich, poor, fat, thin, old, or young, when people end up on my table, and I open them up, I find all people the same on the inside. Judgments I used to make about the way people look or how they appear are now tempered by what I know is on the inside.

"I'm unable to focus on the surface anymore. I see the commonality in all people. We are all the same under the skin. Any bickering we do because of our differences now seems completely ludicrous. Weird, huh?"

"Definitely an unusual perspective, Ellie," I answered, "However, I completely understand how you arrived at it. What I find most remarkable is how you manage to fit all the bits and pieces of your profession into who you are and how you see the world. You are an amazing woman. Thanks for being with us today. You have been incredibly helpful."

She glanced at her wristwatch; three hours had passed. "I should be thanking you. I've complained about not being able to speak honestly about what I've learned or how I feel, and I was a little afraid to show up today. Your invitation was intriguing, but I'm

157

always hesitant to talk about this. I get a strange response oftentimes, even if people say they are interested. It's a lot to digest. I'm grateful you invited me over. Can I come back?"

I laughed. "You are welcome any time."

"Can I bring my husband?"

"Sure. I'd love to meet him."

I walked her to the driveway. We said goodbye, and she promised to visit again.

Back in my studio, Randall and I spoke about the remarkable wisdom Ellie had shared with us. We were impressed and wondered how many people live extraordinary lives yet are seldom asked the most provocative question.

We place so much importance on intellect and education, but we rarely ask what their daily work has taught them about humanity. A goldmine of wisdom lies underneath each diploma or certification of competency. After everyone had cleared out for the day, I sat alone in my garden with a glass of whisky, watching the sunset. I thought back fifty years to my first tragic encounter with death. The image of the tall, thin man in a black suit came to mind.

Images from that summer day were burned into my memory and had haunted my dreams for years. I can still see myself alongside the tracks, standing among my boyhood friends, dumbstruck as we watched the medical examiner do his job.

Ellie had witnessed tragedy that equaled or even surpassed

what I had seen that summer afternoon, yet she'd managed to turn her experience into wisdom instead of nightmares.

Her insight regarding how alike we all were under the skin led me to consider how stubbornly we argued for our differences and caused so much misery in the world. We were born into the world with the same raw material. We lived out our lives in a variety of ways and learned or ignored the lessons presented. Birth, life, and death were a complete package. A package we all had in common.

The Traveling Hat

I'd just got off the phone with my old friend Joe Cryns. He'd asked me to guess what he was wearing. I knew instantly.

The hat.

There were some gaps in our memories. We're old and forgetful. We'd spent considerable time on the phone grinding the gears of memory, trying to get the details right. Getting our story sorted and assembled seemed an appropriate way to pass the time.

Joe was currently doing his best to punch terminal cancer in the face. The following was our best recollection and probably near to the truth.

Years ago, Joe and I learned of a tribal custom from a Lakota elder. If a man admired one of your possessions, you were obligated to give the object to the admirer. Obviously, this custom could be taken to an extreme, and Joe took everything to an extreme. Using this ploy as we traveled, he added a fine leather coat, hats, drums, jewelry, and countless other valuables to his collection of admirable objects.

When Joe called last week, I immediately knew he was wearing a goofy fleece pillbox hat we referred to as the traveling hat. It had gone around the world.

We were certain the hat first landed on Joe's head in London, sometime in the mid-'90s, a gift from an appreciative man who'd admired Joe. I remember a teary-eyed man handing Joe the hat, saying, "This hat will keep your head warm. You're a good bloke. Thanks."

Joe later wore it to a prison workshop we had volunteered to facilitate. Several of the convicts admired it. I reminded Joe of the tribal tradition. He glared at me, reluctant to give up his hat. I insisted and encouraged Joe to be the bigger man. He surrendered it to an appreciative inhabitant of the prison.

The hat did two years behind bars. The men inside used it when attempting to convince a man of his worth. They would seat him in a chair, place it on his head as if it were a crown, and tell him what they admired about him. I guessed the hat kept the man's head from exploding as admiration inflated his heart.

The hat was offered to me after I accidentally commented on

what a beauty it was. The convict who had cared for it said it had done its time, and I should take it over the wall. I figured the hat needed a good airing after prison life, so for the next couple of years, I wore it whenever I went into the woods.

The hat traveled with me to a conference in San Diego, and I slipped it on as I retrieved my baggage. Joe picked me up at the airport, and his first words to me were, "Good to see you, Snake. Nice hat" I handed it over.

Here the details get sketchy.

We knew Jim McCleary (Chicago) and Paul Bates (Brisbane) had each hosted the hat at different times and then passed it on. Maybe more men have had the pleasure? It was hard to say. We were uncertain how many heads it had covered or how many miles it had traveled. I wasn't aware of the latest chapter until Joe filled me in.

Two years ago, an older man visited Joe regularly as he underwent chemo and endured a long hospital stay. The man showed up with two cups of fresh coffee at 6:30 a.m., reliable as clockwork.

Joe said, "You know the kind of guy. Never talks much, and I don't know much about him. He just showed up every day and sat with me. When I was done with treatment and about to be released, I gave him the hat."

Joe's cancer came back with a vengeance a few months ago, and the quiet old man unexpectedly showed up at Joe's bedside, wearing the hat. Of course Joe said, "Nice hat," and it returned to him once again.

It seems appropriate the well-traveled hat admired by so many would end up back on Joe's head. When I last spoke with him, he said he had it on. I have no idea where it ended up after Joe died. I wouldn't be one bit surprised to see the hat in a crowd someday, and when I do, I'll know what to say.

"Nice hat."

The Priest

I met with a priest named Father Bennie today. He has an extraordinary reputation. I've been told he is a human dynamo, the driving force of a small inner-city parish.

The 100-year-old church is located in the worn-thin industrial area of a Midwestern city. Irish and German Catholics first settled the neighborhood in the early 1920s, hard-working immigrants enticed off the farm by the promise of factory-jobs.

Moline Farm Machinery built a large plant in the neighborhood, causing the surrounding landscape to sprout machine shops, foundries, and fabrication shops. Small, modest homes shared space with markets, hardware stores, and corner taverns, where paychecks the bank didn't claim were cashed and spent.

Through the 1950s the neighborhood was a model of American industrial strength.

The factory shut down four decades ago, stripping most of the jobs out of the immediate area. One by one, the markets, hardware stores, and machine shops closed, and twenty-four-hour gas station convenience stores and liquor outlets took their place. The neighborhood looks faded and run down today, as if every surface would benefit from a fresh coat of paint. Poverty, violence, and crumbling buildings blanket the area.

Father Bennie's church hasn't changed all that much over the decades. Originally chartered on a shoestring, Our Lady of the Holy Rosary supports itself on donations, raffles, and Friday night fish dinners. Like many inner-city churches, the congregation is a mix of lifelong members in their 70s and 80s, and a younger generation rich in dreams are willing to spend sweat equity on old run-down homes. Many of the poorest parishioners find shelter in tenements located near the river flats. Holy Rosary and Father Bennie play a critical role in the neighborhood social safety net.

I am touched by how gracious and willing Father Bennie is to make time for me. We rescheduled twice to accommodate his busy schedule, yet our phone calls make me feel as if I am his first priority. I feel honored.

I ring the bell of the rectory, and Father Bennie answers the door. He shakes my hand and welcomes me into the two-story frame house nestled in the shadow of the church. A long oak conference table is prominent in a large central room, and a desk and three walls of bookshelves fill a small office off to the right. A galley kitchen in the rear of the rectory promises coffee, tea, and a stack of cookies on a large platter. We settle across the table from one another.

Father Bennie looks like a priest. On the short side of tall, he carries a few extra pounds, adding bulk to what had probably once been an athletic body.

His blocky torso is topped by a large head sporting wild tufts of gray hair, so common in men who reach beyond sixty. An aging body can make a man take on the presence and sometimes even the appearance of a large boulder.

I can't help staring at his eyes. The deep lines and furrows on his forehead form a platform for long bushy gray eyebrows. Small folds of skin circle bright blue irises, forming small bags that rest one on each cheek. He looks exhausted.

"So, you're here to talk with me about death?" he asks.

"Actually, I want to find out how death has affected you, and what you have learned," I reply.

"I've learned a glass of scotch and a cigar in the evening is soothing," he jokes. Father Bennie smiles across the table, pleased with his own humor. His smile fades slightly as he explains. "I've performed six funerals this week. I guess I am a reluctant expert. Death is an occupational hazard when leading an old parish like

Holy Rosary. The majority of my parishioners are aging. The woman who bakes cookies for me is in her 90s. She's lived down the block for sixty-five years. Twice a week she brings a couple dozen cookies to the rectory." He pats his stomach. "I've asked her to consider low-fat veggie snacks, but she'll have nothing to do with it. She laughed when I suggested it, saying, 'Oh sure, Father, your visitors will appreciate a celery stalk with their coffee.' The topic never came up again. Would you like to take some cookies home?" he asks hopefully.

"Six funerals in one week?" I repeat. "Is that unusual?"

"A little. I've had as many as ten in a week. Three or four is the norm. Death doesn't only visit the aged. Illness, accidents, and violence contribute as well. I end up comforting a lot of families for many reasons. The funeral service represents the end of my work. Usually a lot of drama precedes a death. Illness can take a long time to claim life, but even with sudden death, like a suicide or a shooting, I'm able to see who's in trouble before death arrives.

"Family members ask me to speak with troubled people. They ask if I can help. They're really looking for quick answers. 'How do I fix the problem?' Except there isn't a fix for death. Sudden or prolonged, death will claim us all, but what comes before death? That's where the heavy lifting happens."

"Can you give me an example?"

Father Bennie rubs his tired eyes, using the moment to

massage his memory. "One of my responsibilities is to perform last rites. I'm available four nights a week. The police or hospital calls when they need a priest. I see it as both an honor and a responsibility, but last rites are an example of what I mean by heavy lifting. The prayers aren't arduous, but the experience is. Last rites are about unpacking your bags for the journey and preparing the soul to leave the body. You might imagine what people reveal once they accept death is near. Some are terrified or panicky, and having a priest bedside can be a real comfort. For my own part, being included in the last moments of life is often challenging and always meaningful.

"I was called to the scene of a shooting a month ago. The victim was a young man I'd confirmed several years before. He'd gone wild in his late teens—drinking, drugs, and bad actors for friends. I'd run into him every so often at the diner. We'd share a cup of coffee and talk. I knew he was headed for trouble, but like so many, he had big plans. I'm certain that didn't include being on the wrong side of a drug deal and the victim of a drive-by shooting.

"The police called me at midnight. The shooting took place outside the family home, and his mother insisted the police call me before moving the body.

"It took me twenty minutes to get to the scene. A crowd had gathered, and the mother was standing over her son's body, wailing loudly. The police looked relieved when I arrived. A murder is a gruesome thing to witness. Television doesn't do it justice. She grabbed my arm as I was putting my stole over my head and whispered, 'Father, better put extra oil on that boy's head. He's going to need it to slip through the gates.'

"I run into gallows humor every so often, but even when people are present for a death, they're more often speechless, uncertain what to say or how to act. I first met the boy's mother years ago. A single mom with eight kids and no prospects, she came to the church for help to feed her kids. She's been a regular volunteer for most anything we can dream up for over fifteen years now. She claims her bill will never be paid in full. Still, despite how tough she seems, I often see tears on her cheeks during mass.

"I can't imagine how difficult her life has been. She's lost three of her boys to prison and a son and a daughter to murder. A hard woman. She's had to be. Large doses of tragedy inoculate a person. When the curtain separating security from what frightens us vanishes, we become fully present. So present, we can feel angry, sad, tenderhearted, or even funny, all at once.

Father Bennie brightens. "Would you like a cup of coffee?"

"Sure"

He stands stiffly and walks to the coffee pot. "I see plenty of joy each week," he shouts from the kitchen. "I married a couple last night. Wonderful family. They had a huge champagne reception afterward. Three hundred people! I was out late. I can use the caffeine."

Father Bennie returns and sets a tray between us. Two cups of coffee and a large plate of cookies fill the tray. "Please, help yourself. Any cookies you don't eat go home with you. Just so you know."

He settles in the chair, warming his hands on his mug. He looks me square in the eye. "What exactly are you looking for? Why study death?"

I explain I've had a near brush with death and discovered how little I know about it. I figure I'll talk with people who spend time around death and ask them what they've learned. It turns out I'm not as interested in death as I am in the time just before death occurs. I'm curious about what happens to a person when they're actively dying and the impact on the people around them.

"On call to perform last rites, for instance," I add. "I never thought about it, but of course a priest must be available. Certainly, a system would be set up to summon a priest. Another detail related to dying we seldom talk about."

"You're interested in what we don't speak about?" he inquires.

"Yes. I find it ironic that at sixty years old, I know so little about dying, especially since I have seen people die." "Death wears a different face every time," he comments. "Last Rites are actually three prayers meant to prepare for the journey. Penance, or confession, meant to unburden the soul. Anointing, intended to release physical pain or suffering, and finally, the Eucharist or Viaticum. This last prayer is meant to offer "provisions for the journey." I've said these prayers hundreds, if not thousands of times. Everyone has regrets, pain, or needs provisions. Everyone hears the same prayer, yet each death is unique.

"Sometimes dying comes quickly. More often it lingers, stretching time like a thick rubber band. Loved ones gather for months, flinching, waiting for the band to finally snap.

"If you're really interested in what we don't speak about, I've got a story for you."

"Go ahead," I answer.

Father Bennie stares into his coffee cup. "We don't often talk about the death of a child. It hits everyone hard when children die. I was called late one night to give last rites to a three-year-old.

"A congenital heart defect had made her life little but endless hospital stays and physical misery. Her family and countless doctors had done their best to treat her, but the end was near. No longer responsive to treatment, her parents were forced to make the heart-wrenching decision to end treatment. There was nothing to be done except wait. The doctors were certain she wouldn't last the night.

"I introduced myself to the parents and asked a few questions, mostly to get a read on how they were coping. They were distraught, three years of hope and medical science having run its course.

"They apologetically explained they had been raised Catholic but hadn't belonged to a parish for years. Facing a long uncertain night, they felt it was important to call a priest. I don't always have relationships with the families of the dying, so my feelings were predictably awkward and uncomfortable. After all, I had arrived to perform a most intimate ritual for strangers.

"A mother and father forced by circumstance and human limitations to let go of a child. There would be no redemption. They made the most painful decision a parent can imagine and asked for my help to find some small measure of closure.

"The girl lay sleeping in a jumble of brightly colored blankets, dwarfed by the now silent monitors, pumps, and respirators that had kept her alive the last few months. She woke to my voice, and as I began my prayers, her eyelids fluttered open, revealing large brown eyes. She followed my every movement as I worked my way through the prayers. An impossibly small hand emerged from under the blankets and reached for my pinky finger. 'Do you want something, honey?' I asked. She didn't respond but gripped my finger tightly, watching me with those beautiful eyes.

"As her tiny hand closed on my finger, my heart broke open. Tears clouded my eyes, and prayers I knew by heart suddenly abandoned me. Her body was worn out, and three short years of life doesn't leave much to unpack. She only wanted a hand to hold, or in this case a pinky. The heavy lifting in my life comes in moments like these, when there is nothing to do and my work is to simply "be" with the dying. I completed last rites, but my real service that night was simply to walk a short distance with a little girl grasping my finger.

"The death of a child is so tragic, we avoid talking about it, but children die with a measure of dignity and beauty equal to any adult.

"I can't help feeling especially sad when a child dies. I imagine who they might have become or what they might have accomplished. Dreaming of what might have been leads straight into the abyss. I've learned to accept that death has its own timing, and age has little bearing on the whole event.

"Do you want another cup of coffee?" he asks.

I nod, and he heads for the coffee pot. I am fully in the afterglow of his story. I take a ginger cookie off the plate, break it in half, and nibble as I consider the tender heart of this man.

He returns after few minutes but doesn't take a seat. He wanders around the room, clutching his mug as he gently lectures.

"I don't want you to get the idea that a priest's life is all late-night drama. People call a priest to serve in a variety of ways: baptisms, confirmation, weddings, and mass. The late-night call is a fundamental yet small part of an exceptionally broad-mission.

"I've been fortunate to witness the full spectrum of life. My parishioners offer up whole rivers of life. My role is to wade in with them. I hope I bring some wisdom and comfort, whether life offers up celebration or tragedy. I suffer highs and lows like anyone else, but I've had to become emotionally agile to serve my parish."

"Emotionally agile?" I ask, curious what he means by the term.

"The child's parents asked me to perform a funeral mass three days later. It was heartbreaking to see that little white casket. After the funeral I attended a retirement party, followed by a birthday party for a ninety-six-year-old woman, and finished the evening with a wedding ceremony and a dance. The only way I'm able to move through the variety of events I attend in a day is to be emotionally agile.

"Each day asks something different from me. I don't have the luxury of losing myself in sadness, angry or resentful over what I can't change. I'm sad at a funeral, happy to celebrate a birthday, and grateful to be considered family at a wedding. I experience all those feelings and more in one day. People expect me to meet them where they are, and I'm glad to do it, but you must understand the speed with which emotion-provoking situations flow through my life. Look in the dictionary under "emotional agility," and you'll see my picture."

Father Bennie smiles proudly and refers to a book he read years ago, touting the virtues of "emotional intelligence." He thinks the author is slightly off base, stressing intelligence as if emotion is simply something to train and keep on a leash.

Self-knowledge and discipline are essential, but the willingness to feel emotion is where we mature our humanity and connect to spirit. Father Bennie feels emotions have less to do with intelligence and more to do with fully experiencing life.

He adds, "I've occupied a front row seat for all the humanity and spirit a man could imagine."

He sits in the chair opposite me. "What I've learned comes from more than just being there at the end. I've learned to appreciate every bit of life, birth to death. The good, the bad, and the ugly, I serve people in need or suffering, and I celebrate with them as well. Can I change the subject? Another story just came to mind, and I think you might appreciate it."

"Sure, but I don't want to take too much of your time. You've already been generous."

I barely get the words out of my mouth before he's off, telling me how he leads tours to holy shrines around the world.

He speeds through a summary of the places he's visited and speaks of a recent tour to India. Two weeks into the tour, he sent his group off with a local priest for the day. Having seen the slums of Calcutta many times as a tour guide, he decided on a day-long solo journey. After the priest took his place, Father Bennie went off by himself, intending to meet Mother Teresa face to face.

"I knocked on Mother Teresa's door and waited in the dusty

entrance, listening to the sound of footsteps approaching. An impossibly small nun opened the door, smiled warmly, and said, 'Welcome, we've been expecting you.'

"I was caught off guard. I hadn't made an appointment. I wasn't aware of any formal process for visiting her. I just knocked on her door. She ushered me in and said, 'Mother Teresa will be with you presently.'

"She walked in a few minutes later, greeting me with one hand outstretched. 'I've been looking forward to meeting you. Would you like a cup of tea?'

"I was confused but followed her to a small hotplate, where she prepared the tea. I was utterly baffled by the notion that she had been expecting me.

I explained that I had always wanted to meet her and admired the work she had accomplished. We settled at a table with our teacups, speaking of our ministries and what we were engaged in. She showed significant interest in the work I was undertaking in serving an old inner-city parish.

"Well into our conversation, she said, 'Can I ask you a question?'

"'Yes,' I replied.

"'Would you agree to come work with me here in Calcutta?'

"The gravity of her offer swept over me like a tsunami. I'm an ordinary priest. A chance to work with Mother Teresa? I couldn't believe my ears. Yet she was sitting in front of me expectantly, waiting for my answer.

"The tsunami receded as my life in Minnesota and commitment to my parish swam back into focus. A flattering offer, but I had obligations. I told her how honored I was that she had asked, but I had to say no. Many people at home were counting on my commitment.

"Mother Teresa listened intently. 'I understand. However, would you promise me one thing?'

"'Certainly.' "'Wherever you end up, promise you'll find your own Calcutta?' She focused on me intently as she waited for my response.

"'Yes,' I said. 'I promise.'

"I spent over an hour with her. She was a humble yet powerful person and ruthlessly clear about her mission. We ended our visit with a prayer, and I felt like a lucky man as I walked through the streets back to my hotel. I was glowing. Mother Teresa had asked me to work with her!

"I was still in a pleasant form of rapture by the time I met the tour participants for drinks that evening. I shared my story of meeting her with several people gathered around the bar, and we speculated about how she might have known I would visit.

"The waiter announced our table was ready, and as the crowd filed into the dining room, the priest who had led the group for me during the day put a hand on my shoulder and whispered in my ear. 'You should know. Mother Teresa greets every visitor that way and offers them all a job.'

"'What?' I replied, suddenly feeling betrayed and appropriately deflated.

"'Yes,' he continued. 'She is sincere. She did anticipate your arrival and did make a genuine job offer. Just not in the way you imagined. Shall we join the others for dinner?'

"He winked at me and walked away, joining the others in the dining room, leaving me alone at the bar, mystified."

He finishes his story. I have been watching his eyes. I'm sure he was exhausted. His eyelids closed occasionally, as if he were falling asleep, yet he never missed a beat. His eyes had seen duty in Vietnam, tragedies of many stripes, drug addiction, crime, and violence. His eyes had offered compassion to countless grieving families and blessed hundreds of young families just starting out.

My fascination with his weary eyes suddenly make sense. I recall what is so familiar and comforting about them. They are the same eyes I remember from a photo I've seen of Mother Teresa. Wise, compassionate, and more significant, they have grown old and wrinkled from looking at life unflinchingly.

"My Mother Theresa story is a favorite," he says. "I serve my Calcutta every day. Meeting people where they are. Sometimes a little extra oil or a pinky finger, sometimes a blessing for a new couple, sometimes a painfully honest conversation. I serve wherever I'm needed."

He places his hands palms down on the table and leans forward. His face grows serious. "Let me be clear regarding what I've learned about death. That's what you came for, not simply to be entertained by a priest full of stories.

"We've all pondered death. Questions like what happens after? Is there any after?

"The silent or taboo conversation in our culture is not about dying but how we find our way to 'dead' remains unspoken. It's necessary to separate dead from dying, and when we do, the conversation gets meaningful and complicated.

"We'd like to believe dying will pass in the blink of an eye. Maybe the light will go out in the throes of passion or we manage to drop over suddenly while cresting the summit of a beautiful mountain. Great images, but how realistic are they?" He slaps the table for emphasis. "The truth is dying takes time, months or even years. Much of this time, we may be entirely reliant on others. Fear of pain or prolonged illness is a common theme or concern. Being confined to a bed or being alone ranks right up there too, and this explains why we avoid the discussion.

"A depressing topic, and truthfully death is frightening in its uncertainty.

"Planning for death is foolish and does little to satisfy or comfort. It's not as if we can pack a bag. Preparing takes a very different form for this trip.

"Don't get me wrong, I hope you go in a blaze of glory, but realistically for most, dying is a slow walk, not a sprint. It's is packed with vulnerability, loss of control, gratitude, regret, love, relationships, confusion, and uncertainty. Dying would be "packed" with everything we experience in life. It's not separate from life. It is the end of it.

"Something you should know is that people tend to die in a manner congruent with how they lived their lives. Fearful or courageous, loving or selfish, our bags are already packed. The suitcase we grab will look familiar."

Father Bennie pauses, letting his words sink in, and suddenly points at my chest, demanding in a firm voice, "How do you suppose your dying will look?" he asked. "Would you change anything?"

"W-Well," I stammer, "of course I'd change, if ... but...I'm uncertain what to say."

He winks at me and relaxes with a sly smile, fully appreciating my discomfort before continuing. "If you die in the same way you live your life, why not make it easy on yourself? Live a good life and die a good death. Seems simple enough.

"I wonder if the reasonable approach to preparation comes down to making a choice, with our eyes wide open and curious or shut tight, gripping the wheel with both hands? So, you see how my Calcutta story fits.

"Mother Theresa's words —'Find your Calcutta wherever you go'—helped me see clearly. Birth, death, and everything in between, everything I feel and the support I offer, are all about living a generous life with my eyes open, able to recognize the Calcutta in front of me wherever I wander. It makes a person wonder why so many of us resist living fully in the moment. I figure my bags are packed.

"Speaking of which, I have to say goodbye, I have home visits to make this afternoon."

I thank him for his time and attention. He loads me up with a paper bag full of cookies and walks me to the door. We say goodbye, and on the way out, he hands me a pile of church newsletters containing a weekly column he writes for parishioners. "More stories," he says.

I drive slowly through the old neighborhood on my way home, paying special attention to the shuttered warehouses, empty storefronts, and chipped layers of paint on the houses in Father Bennie's Calcutta.

The Return

Decades have passed since I paddled Harper's old canoe across the lake, searching for my purpose. The years have worn me thin, and I often find myself the oldest man in the room. Sadly, all the wise men who launched me into the dark that night are buried, resting beneath the ancient white pines on Harper's bluff. I miss them.

I returned from my solo journey that October afternoon thirty years ago to see the old men gathered at the water's edge, grinning. They beached the canoe with rough hands and steadied me until I regained my land legs.

Sam, laughing, pointed in my direction as I stumbled across the stones, "Look! The lake has transformed him into a newborn fawn and spit him back on shore." After twenty-two hours of riding the swells, the upset to my equilibrium took its sweet time to recede.

Harper herded us into the narrow canyon and onto the lift three at a time for the ascent to the deck. Art sat me down at the stone counter in the cabin, with a bowl of stew and a large slice of cornbread slathered with butter, while Lloyd poured a large mug of fresh-pressed cider, suggesting I relax, clean up, and when I was ready, come join them. "We still have work to do."

I'd been afraid of this. They were going to ask me if I'd found my purpose, and hard as I tried, I'd come back empty. An entire night on the lake, and confusion was all I'd brought back with me. The stew left a sour lump in my stomach as I imagined how much time and intention the men had lavished on me. I hated to disappoint them.

When I could linger no longer in the hot shower, I dressed and joined them on the deck in the twilight. They were sharing a bottle of scotch. Sam patted the arm of the wicker chair next to him and motioned for me to sit down. Coals glowed orange in a large cast iron pot in the center of the circle, and Art fed fresh cedar tips into it.

"The lake was kind to you last night," Harper said. "Not everyone is so lucky, Harlan was hit with a hail storm when he went out, and to this day, if you run your hand over his skull, you'll find more dimples than a golf ball. Art launched late in the year, and when he returned, ice had formed in the night, separating him from shore. He had to break his way back to shore with a paddle. The lake gifted you with beautiful Indian Summer weather and rocked your canoe with a gentle hand. Consider it a blessing."

His words caused me to feel worse. I'd been let off easy. Sure, my arms still felt like jelly from the constant paddling required to keep the current from carrying me to Canada, and my skin had been burned raw by the autumn sun, but I wondered if my purpose had remained elusive because I hadn't suffered enough.

Harper said, "We held you in our hearts and minds as you paddled in the dark, and we welcome you back."

"I still don't know!" I blurted. "I tried but I'm no closer to an understanding of what my purpose is than when you shoved me into that water. The lake didn't speak to me, and I feel like you've wasted your time. I'm sorry."

Sam placed a hand on my shoulder, looked into my eyes, and said, "Good! Now we can really welcome you home."

Bewildered, I felt angry. Damn Harper and his constant riddling. They send me searching for purpose, and when I return empty-handed, they're pleased. Each time I visit these men, I return home confused about what I brushed up against. Are they screwing with me for a good laugh or loving me?

"Please explain," I said. "I've been afraid to tell you I'd failed. Now it sounds like you're all pleased. I don't get it."

"I sort of misled you," Harper said with a crafty smile.

"There's far more to the lesson than meets the eye. I asked you to trust me and follow my instructions, and you've done well. We offered you the gift of an initiation, and we aren't finished. A bit of patience is called for. Listen to what we have to say. You will understand.

"When I first asked you to question your direction and purpose, I did so out of genuine concern. I was certain you were getting too comfortable. I see something in you that may languish if you fall asleep. I let you think you were on a search for purpose, but what will benefit you most is understanding."

"Begin with the fact that initiation repeats over a lifetime, and it's wise to recognize the ancient four-step process. The first three stages of initiation, separation, descent, and ordeal, appear with regular frequency. A separation from the familiar, followed by a descent into the unknown, and finally an ordeal wrestling with the challenge.

"The fourth stage—the return—completes the process. We are here to welcome you home, but don't expect a parade and a slap on the back. You still have work to do before we bring all this to an end. Are you willing?"

"Do I have to go out in the canoe again?" Harper laughed. "No. The return takes place here and now. Are you willing?"

"Yes," I replied, curious what they had in store for me.

Sam stood up and gripped the deck railing, staring out over

the lake. With his back to us, he began a story.

"I was an army medic in Vietnam, drafted at age eighteen. I was big and strong, so they figured I'd be well suited to dragging wounded out of the jungle. Despite my best efforts, I watched too many young men die." Sam turned around and faced us, tears streaming down his cheeks. "I was in rough shape when I returned home.

"The war was so controversial, many of us refused to even say we'd served to avoid the harsh criticism people had about it. Angry and confused, I withdrew and found comfort in the deep woods. I took a job cutting trees and spent my days hauling logs out of the brush with chains and a bulldozer. It was exhausting work, and on payday the whole crew would go to town and drink away our paychecks.

"One Saturday night a drunken loudmouth discovered I'd been in the army, and he started giving me shit. I snapped. It took six grown men to pull me off the guy, and I'm grateful they stopped me, or I would have killed him. A couple of elders were in the bar that night and saw the whole thing, and the next day, four of them showed up at the logging camp, looking for me.

"Harlan's father was one of them. I remembered him from ceremonies I'd attended as a boy. I'll never forget his words to me that afternoon. 'It's time to come home from the war. Let us help you.'" Sam sat down, and after a long silence continued his story.

"They launched me onto the lake one evening. They told me to paddle out and ask the lake to soothe the scar war had left on my heart.

"A strong southeast wind blew offshore that night, whipping spray off the whitecaps, and in no time, I was drenched to the bone and shivering. I was strong back then and paddled like a demon to reach the place where sky and water erase all sign of land. I rode six-foot swells for hours, until the clouds racing across the sky parted and a half moon lit the water.

"I tried to convince myself it was just a large lake trout surfacing next to my canoe when I looked over the side and saw the first face float by. My mind scrambled to make sense of it, unable to comprehend what the lake had offered up.

"The surface unexpectedly grew still, and I quit paddling, lulled by the current and mesmerized by countless moonlit faces floating just beneath the surface. I recognized each face.

"I'd tended to many during the war as they encountered the seam where life and death are stitched together. Some survived the violence done to their bodies, and some did not. As their faces floated closely around my canoe, a peculiar calm replaced my initial alarm. No hint of pain or suffering showed on any face, nor did I feel any fear. The faces appeared sanguine and slowly circled my canoe, seemingly determined to convey something.

"No words were spoken. Spirits speak mysterious languages,

but there was no mistaking their message. They were grateful. Grateful I'd tended their wounds and offered compassion when they were afraid. Together we had peered deep into the dark without the luxury of looking away, and the experience had earned their gratitude.

"I wept for hours. The currents rocked me gently through the night as I lay in the bottom of the canoe. The faces disappeared at dawn, but the gratitude they generously offered that night washed the shell from my heart and stayed with me for life."

Art spread more cedar tips on top of the coals, and we sat quietly, digesting Sam's story as the sweet smoke circled us.

"Sam thought he'd returned empty-handed." Harper said, breaking the silence. "When he came off the lake, he wasn't sure what to make of his experience. We've each spent solo time out there and have learned the rare times the lake does speak, she addresses the soul and not the mind. Understanding comes with time, because the soul must savor what the lake offers up."

Lloyd agreed. "Patience is the key. We share an obligation to pass along what the old men offered us. The two questions they asked ring as true for me today as they did years ago. The questions of the return.

"A long life will repeat the ancient rhythm of separation, descent, and ordeal because all things change. It is a responsibility and privilege to fully participate in change. Resistance is futile."

Lloyd smiled. "The old men taught us to recognize and respect the rhythm of change, but they also encouraged us to distill wisdom from each ordeal. The two questions of the return are intended to nurture wisdom and must not be answered quickly, but considered carefully over time, so the mind and the soul can both weigh in. Harper will ask the questions.

Harper locked eyes with me. "What did you learn? How will we all benefit? Don't answer!" he warned, pointing at me. "Go home and see what grows inside you. And welcome back," he added with a broad grin.

Art poured me a bit of scotch, and all five men raised a glass to toast my return. We sat on the deck late into the night, joking and sharing stories. I was thankful they had taken me under their wings and grateful for their friendship.

I left my mother's house at sixteen and wandered the world in search of wisdom. Fifty years down the road, I've stumbled across a fair amount. Little compares with the potency of the two questions posed upon our return from the ordeal.

"What did you learn?"

"How will we all benefit?"

Wisdom: the ability to learn from life and use the knowledge gained to shape the future for the good of all.

Bears Play Poker

Northern Minnesota, where 1700 square miles of wilderness are sprinkled with cold blue lakes, granite boulders, pine-poplar, and tamarack. Loons call across the lake at dusk, and owls glide silently through the dark forest. Hidden from view, bears play poker with wolves under a canopy of stars.

Seeking the company of honest men, twenty of us circled up under the stars for a week, ages fifty-seven to seventy-six. When men pass the age of fifty, fighting the corrosion of ego becomes a futile exercise. We accept that life rusts a man and thins his armor. Soul is found right under the surface.

As we stumble among rocks and roots on unreliable feet, hands reach out to steady us. When water is too heavy for one man to carry, another pair of hands appear, and when a word is too faint to hear, we shout at one another.

The years grow a willingness to watch out for one another. The camp ritual of chopping wood and carrying water hasn't changed, but the tenderness and companionship between men has matured. We know love.

Twenty-five years ago, we brought our boys to Fall Lake, but our sons are now grown men with children of their own. I appreciate the man and father my son has become, yet I miss the curious boy who once wandered the woods beside me.

Two old men go for a swim. Both over seventy and friends for thirty years, they held hands and shuffled into the lake on tender feet. Bare butt naked and droopy in all the usual places, they threaded a cautious path between the slippery boulders and paused.

Crotch deep and grinning like fools, they lean forward stiff legged. Pale old trees splash under the dark water only to surface moments later, sputtering like ten-year-olds.

Between sobering conversations regarding what we've learned about life, and wet old men laughing in a lake, I saw beauty. I grow melancholic when my time in the woods comes to an end.

Northern Minnesota, sprinkled with cold blue lakes, granite boulders, pine-poplar and tamarack. Loons call across the lake at dusk, and owls glide silently through the dark forest. Hidden from view, bears play poker with wolves under a canopy of stars.

81330849R00113

Made in the USA
San Bernardino, CA
06 July 2018